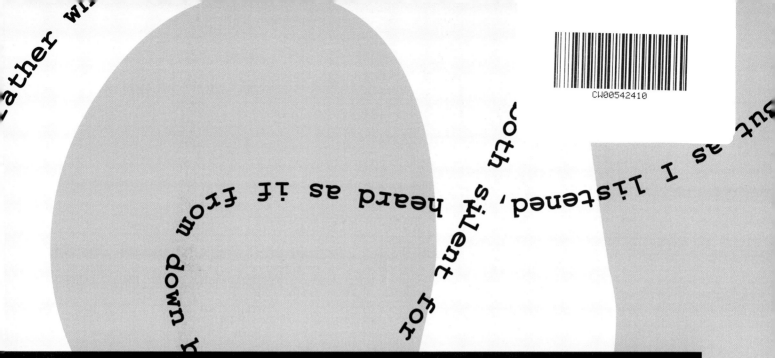

Skills for Writing

Unit 1: Alter egos Emma Curran
Unit 2: Writing the world Helen Lines
Series consultant: Debra Myhill

PEARSON

CW00542410

Published by Pearson Education Limited, Edinburgh Gate, Harlow, Essex, CM20 2JE.

www.pearsonschoolsandfecolleges.co.uk

Text © Pearson Education Limited 2014
Typeset by Jerry Udall and Tek-Art

The rights of Helen Lines and Emma Curran to be identified as authors of this work has been asserted by them in accordance with the Copyright, Designs and Patents Act 1988.

First published 2014

17 16 15
10 9 8 7 6 5 4

British Library Cataloguing in Publication Data
A catalogue record for this book is available from the British Library

ISBN 9781447948759

Printed in Italy by Lego S.p.a

Acknowledgements

We would like to thank Debra Myhill at the University of Exeter for her invaluable help in the development of this course.

The author and publisher would like to thank the following individuals and organisations for permission to reproduce photographs:

(Key: b-bottom; c-centre; l-left; r-right; t-top)
Alamy Images: Bhandol 60, Cultura Creative 65, 75b, Francois Gotier / VWPics 54b, l), Russell Milner 44, 70tr; **Ardea:** Yann Arthus-Bertrand 59; **BBC Photo Library:** 43tl, 43br, 50c, 62; **Corbis:** 46b, Alain Nogues / Sygma 70br, Douglas Ziegler / Splash News 74b, Jo Prichard / epa 50l, Steve Gorton 53b, Stringer / Indonesia / Reuters 74l; **DK Images:** Geoff Brightline / Peter Minister - modelmaker 49, Nigel Hicks 71tr; **Getty Images:** 68t, 74r, Barcroft Media 56t, Cultura / Liam Norris 19, Hristo Shindov 1, 25, Juanmonino 32, Redferns 2c, Wire Image 75t, WireImage 2r, 3l; **Nature Picture Library:** Anup Shah 50tr; **Pearson Education Ltd:** Sozaijiten 48tl, 76; **Photos.com:** TommyIX 30r, Velirina 16r, **Rex Features:** Brian J Ritchie 2l, Paramount Everett 3c, Stratraks 3r, Warner Bros / Everett 17, 26; **Science Photo Library Ltd:** NASA 48tr; **Shutterstock.com:** Andrew Burgess 11, 15, AntonSokolov 33, Balu 70tl, Dr Morley Read 52, Geoffrey Kuchera 56b, 68b, Kamnuan 16l, Kati Neudert 28r, Linn Cuirie 12, Maria Dryfhout 9c, maxstockphoto 67, Mikhail hoboton Popov 29r, Mogens Troile 9l, 9r, Nagel Photography 56c, Sergei Aleshin 54r, Stu Porter 42, 53 (UO), Tyler Olson 39t, Yanlev iv (prelims), Yuriy Kulik 13; **The Kobal Collection:** Summit Entertainment 35br, **Veer/Corbis:** Andrey Kravchenko 28l, Dany Hooks 71tl, dngood 8r, ecopic 46t, ia_64 36, Lusoimages.com 5l, Mino21 38br, Sandra van der Steen 5r, sebikus 7, Solarseven 54l, Ulrich Mueller 70bl; **www.imagesource.com:** CORBIS / BRIDGE 29l

All other images © Pearson Education

We are grateful to the following for permission to reproduce copyright material:

Figures
Figure on page 4 and 6 from *http://www.culture24.org.uk/art/art67432 The Witches, by Roald Dahl*, The Random House Group (UK), The Estate of Roald Dahl; Figure on page 10 from *Kafka, Franz, Metamorphosis and Other Stories, Translated by Michael Hoffman (Penguin Books: London, 2007);* Figure on page 22 and 24 from *Shan, Darren, The Saga of Darren Shan, Vampire Blood Triology, Cirque Du Freak (HarperCollins: London, 2000) ISBN-13: 978-0006754169;* Figure on page 43 from *Frozen Planet: A World Beyond Imagination*, by Alastair Fothergill, published by BBC Books. Reprinted by permission of The Random House Group Limited;

Logos
Logo on page 62 from Greenpeace, with permission from Greenpeace UK; Logo on page 62 from Friends of the Earth (England, Wales & N. Ireland), www.foe.co.uk; Logo on page 62 from RSPB; Logo on page 69 from www.simple-green-living.com/image-files/carbonfootpint.jpg, with permission from Simple Green Living; Logo on page 75 from Think.Eat.Save, www.thinkeatsave.org,Save Food Initiative.

Text
Extracts on page 4, 6, 14, 17 and 26 from *The Witches, by Roald Dahl ISBN-13: 978-0141346410 Puffin p.6*, with permission from David Higham Associates Limited; Extract on page 7 from *Rapunzel, A First Book of Fairy Tales, Stories retold by Mary Hoffman, illustrated by Julie Downing (Dorling Kindersley Limited, London, 2001, 2006), p16*, copyright © Dorling Kindersley, 2001 and Copyright © Mary Hofman 2001,2006. Reproduced by permission of the author c/o Rogers,Coleridge & White Ltd.,20 Powis Mews, London W11 1JN; Extract on pages 10 and 14 is approx.185 words from *Kafka, Franz, Metamorphosis and Other Stories, Translated by Michael Hoffman (Penguin Books: London, 2007)*, translation copyright © Michael Hofmann, 2007 and "Metamorphosis", from METAMORPHOSIS AND OTHER STORIES by Franz Kafka, translated by Michael Hofmann, translation copyright (c) 2007 by Michael Hofmann, Used by permission of Penguin, a division of Penguin Group (USA) LLC; Extracts on page 22, 24, 27, 30 and 37 from from *Shan, Darren, The Saga of Darren Shan, Vampire Blood Triology, Cirque Du Freak (HarperCollins: London, 2000) ISBN-13: 978-0006754169*, reprinted by permission of HarperCollins Publishers Ltd © 2000 *Shan, Darren* Ltd and The Christopher Little Literary Agency LLP; Extract on page 32, Copyright © 2011 Martyn Bedford, from FLIP by Martyn Bedford, reproduced by permission of Walker Books Ltd, London SE11 5HJ www.walker.co.uk; All rights reserved; Extracts on 34 from *Eat Shoots and Leaves* Profile Books (Lynne Truss, 2003) p.9; Extract on page 35 from *Meyer, Stephanie, Twilight (Atom: London, 2006) ISBN-978-1904233657*, Little, Brown Book Group (UK) and From TWILIGHT by Stephanie Meyer, copyright © 2005 by Stephanie Meyer. By permission of Little, Brown and Company. All rights reserved; Extract on page 44 from interview with March of the Penguins Director Luc Jacquet,News.nationalgeographic.co.uk/news/2005/06/0624_050624_marchpenguin.html Stefan Lovgren for National Geographic News, 24 June 2005, Stefan Lovgren/National Geographic Creative; Quote A on page 48 from James B. Irwin, Apollo 15, with permission from Mary Ellen Irwin-Vickers; Quote B on page 48 from Edgar D. Mitchell; Extracts on page 48 and 49 from *Life on Earth*, HarperCollins (Attenborough, D. 1979), with permission from David Attenborough Productions Ltd; Extract A on page 49 from Ten arms and an eye, The Unmuseum, www.unmuseum.mus.pa.us, with permission from Lee Krystek; Extract B on page 49 from *Sharks: Silent Hunters of the Deep*, Reader's Digest (Taylor, R. and Taylor, V. 1987), with permission from The Reader's Digest Association Inc; Extract at the bottom of page 49 from Lifesense by John Downer, published by BBC Books. Reprinted by permission of The Random House Group Limited; Extract on page 51 adapted from *In the Shadow of Man* by Jane Goodall, copyright © 1971 by Hugo and Jane van Lawick-Goodall. Used by permission of Houghton Mifflin Harcourt Publishing Company. All rights reserved; Voiceover extract on page 53 from BBC Nature: Wildlife - Speed Sensation: Inside the Perfect Predator, www.bbc.co.uk/nature/life/Cheetah#p00715gc; Extract on page 57 from BBC Natural World: 'Danger in Paradise. End of the Road?', transcribed from BBC Nature Video Collectionswww.bbc.co.uk/naturecollections/p0063wt7; Extract on page 65 after Town dumps plastic bags,http://www.bbc.co.uk/devon/content/articles/2007/05/01/modbury_plastic_bags_feature.shtml; Extract on page 65 quotes in the article Town dumps plastic bags, http://www.bbc.co.uk/devon/content/articles/2007/05/01/modbury_plastic_bags_feature.shtml, with permission from Rebecca Hosking; Extracts A – E on page 75 from www.thinkeatsave.org, Save Food initiative; Extract on page 78 from Campaign Writing Tips, http://www.rspca.org.uk/education

Every effort has been made to contact copyright holders of material reproduced in this book. Any omissions will be rectified in subsequent printings if notice is given to the publishers.

Contents

Skills for Writing

Skills for Writing is a unique digital, print and training solution. Developed in partnership with Professor Debra Myhill and her team from the University of Exeter, it embeds the principles of the Grammar for Writing pedagogy – trialled and proven to accelerate the rate of writing progress significantly.

ActiveTeach: interactive front-of-class teaching

ActiveTeach Presentation is our digital front-of-class teaching tool, providing you with the book on-screen and a wealth of additional interactive resources to help you embed the Grammar for Writing pedagogy.

Real text extracts introduce students to the choices that authors make in order to create certain effects in their writing.

The Writer's Workshop area guides students through the grammatical choices writers make and the effects they create.

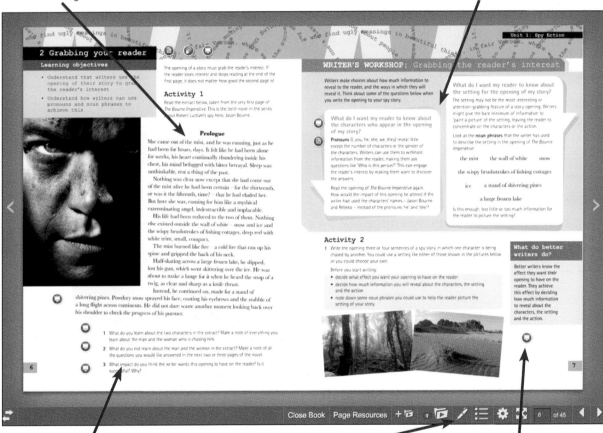

Each page is divided into zoom areas, allowing you to enlarge and annotate each section using the annotation tool.

The annotation tool can be used to identify effective use of language and to record students' responses to an extract.

Hotspot icons link to resources for each lesson, including PowerPoints, worksheets, videos and interactive activities.

Teacher guide

The lesson plans in the teacher guide take you through all you need to teach a Skills for Writing lesson. The lessons guide you through the activities in the student book explaining the effect that is being focused on, providing additional support on the grammatical concepts covered and referring to the relevant resources from ActiveTeach. Extra activities for students needing more support or challenge are also suggested in every lesson plan – ideal for differentiating the learning.

ActiveLearn: online, independent learning

ActiveLearn includes **ActiveBooks** and an **ActiveCourse** that provides your students with a range of independent digital learning exercises for completion as homework. Linking closely to the learning focus of the in-class teaching, these exercises are carefully designed to consolidate and boost understanding and to motivate students to become more independent learners and writers.

Digital homework activities allow students to consolidate and test their understanding of the grammar features that have been focused on in class.

Students are given three attempts at each activity, with hints and tips to motivate them after each attempt.

Independent writing activities encourage students to practise writing and then to reflect on the language choices they have made.

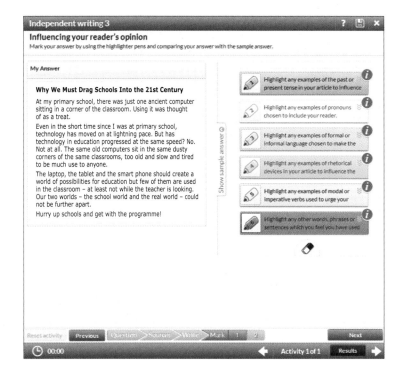

ActiveLearn also provides you with detailed reporting on how students are performing, enabling you to track and monitor progress in writing.

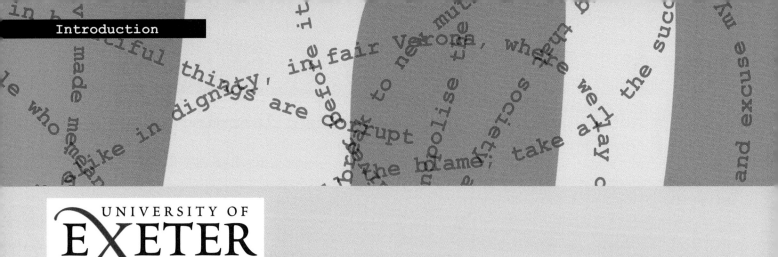

UNIVERSITY OF
EXETER

Learning to write is about learning to be powerful. When you can write confidently, you can make things happen: you can campaign for things that matter to you; you can present yourself and your personality in writing for job or university applications; you can express your deepest, most personal feelings; you can write stories and poems that make others laugh or weep. In fact, you can write to change the world!

This book is to help you become a confident, powerful writer. It sets out to show you how authors create and convey different meanings in their writing by the choices they make, and invites you to consider how the meaning might have been subtly different had they made different choices. The book is very clear about how you can become a better writer, but it is not a recipe book or set of instructions for success. Writing is far more complex than that. We want you to think like a writer, knowing what choices and possibilities you have in each piece of writing, and being able to make and justify those choices with confidence. Enjoy the power!

Debora Myhill

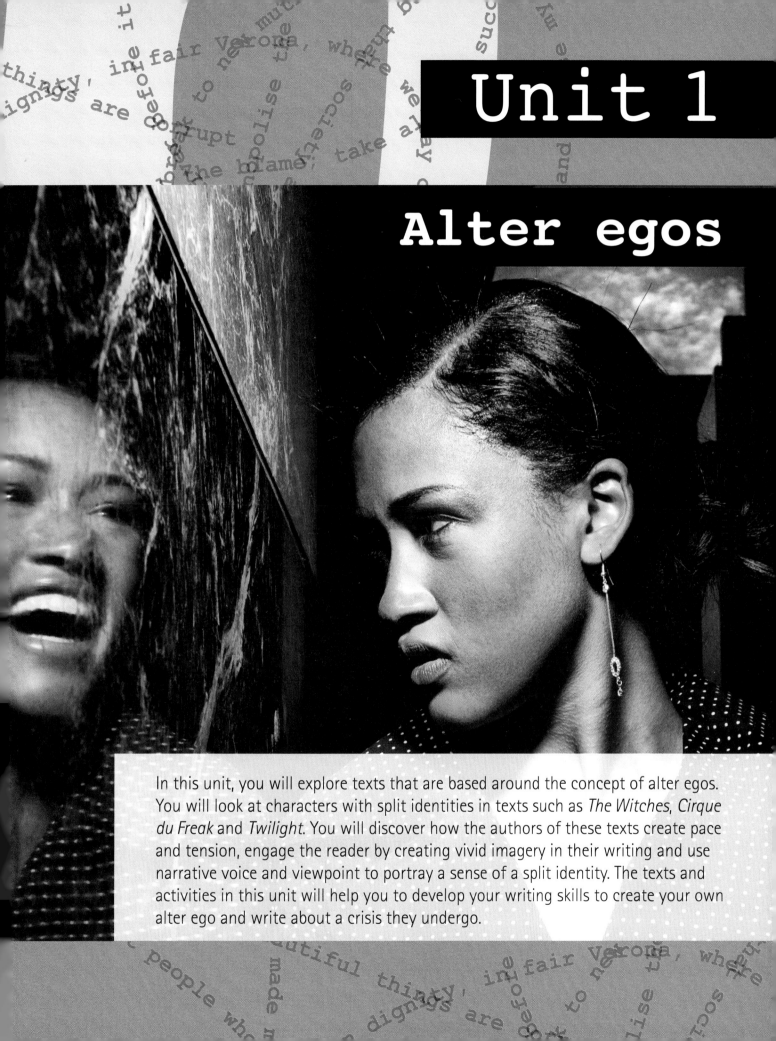

Unit 1

Alter egos

In this unit, you will explore texts that are based around the concept of alter egos. You will look at characters with split identities in texts such as *The Witches*, *Cirque du Freak* and *Twilight*. You will discover how the authors of these texts create pace and tension, engage the reader by creating vivid imagery in their writing and use narrative voice and viewpoint to portray a sense of a split identity. The texts and activities in this unit will help you to develop your writing skills to create your own alter ego and write about a crisis they undergo.

1 Discovering a hidden self

Learning objective

- Understand the concept of an alter ego

An alter ego is a person's secondary or alternative personality. In Latin, it translates as 'other self'; it is like having a hidden self.

Activity 1

Lots of singers have an alter ego, for example: Eminem and Slim Shady; Beyonce Knowles and Sasha Fierce; Katy Perry and Kathy Beth Terry.

Alter egos can be good or bad characters; they can have super powers such as Clark Kent's alter ego, Superman, who fights against evil, or they might be an evil force in itself, like Mr Hyde. An alter ego allows you to have a different self, which enables you to explore an alternative world.

1   Why do you think the people pictured above might wish to have an alter ego?

2   Think of some fictional characters who transform into their alter egos (for example, Clark Kent's alter ego is Superman, Bruce Wayne's is Batman, Dr Jekyll's is Mr Hyde).

3   a List the qualities of one or two of the characters that you have noted down and then the qualities of their alter ego.
    For an example, look at the box opposite:

Character	Alter ego
Clark Kent	Superman
shy	confident
clumsy	powerful
bumbling	superhuman
quiet	strong
hardworking	caring
kind	

b   What are the differences between the qualities of the character and their alter ego? How is the author using the concept of the alter ego?

What do better writers do?

Better writers use the concept of an alter ego to explore the hidden selves of their characters and the alternative worlds in which they might live.

Activity 2

1   Think of an alter ego that you would like to have, or invent an alter ego for someone you know, e.g. a teacher, a dinner lady, your doctor or a family pet.

2   Write down what your alter ego would be like using the following questions to help you.

- What qualities would your alter ego have?
- Do they have any super powers?
- Would they be a force for good or evil or perhaps both?
- Does he/she/it have any more sinister characteristics?
- Does your alter ego look any different from his/her/its other self?

3   Highlight any key words/phrases that you have used which you think most effectively describe your alter ego.

Activity 3

Use your notes from Activity 2 to write a short description of your imagined alter ego.

Before you start writing think about:

- how you will introduce your alter ego effectively
- the language that you will use to describe the key characteristics of your alter ego
- the setting in which you might wish to place your alter ego
- how you want your reader to respond to him/her/it.

Learning objective

- Understand how writers use repeated noun phrases and imperatives to create a sense of authority and engage the reader

Some characters in children's literature have alter egos, such as the witches in Roald Dahl's *The Witches* who disguise themselves as 'ordinary women' with 'ordinary jobs' who are secretly trying to entrap children and 'squelch' them.

Activity 1

Read the extract below from the opening of *The Witches*.

In fairy-tales, witches always wear silly black hats and black cloaks, and they ride on broomsticks.

But this is not a fairy-tale. This is about REAL WITCHES.

The most important thing you should know about REAL WITCHES is this. Listen very carefully. Never forget what is coming next.

REAL WITCHES dress in ordinary clothes and look very much like ordinary women. They live in ordinary houses and they work in ORDINARY JOBS.

That is why they are hard to catch.

A REAL WITCH hates children with a red-hot sizzling hatred that is more sizzling and red-hot than any hatred you could possibly imagine.

1   Look how the narrator describes the witches of fairy tales.

In fairy-tales, witches always wear silly black hats and black cloaks, and they ride on broomsticks.

   a What are some other common characteristics of witches from fairy tales?
   b In what ways are these fairy tale witches so obviously not real?

2   Now look at how the writer describes the witches in this extract.

REAL WITCHES dress in ordinary clothes and look very much like ordinary women. They live in ordinary houses and they work in ORDINARY JOBS.

   a How do these witches differ from the witches of fairy tales?
   b What does this suggest about the difference between this narrative and a fairy tale?

WRITER'S WORKSHOP: Engaging the reader

Writers, and particularly children's writers, spend a lot of time making their stories sound as real as possible – even if those stories include witches, wizards or other strange beings. One technique that writers use to engage the reader is to ask them to 'suspend their disbelief' and to trust in the story they are about to hear.

How can I create a tone of authority in my narrative?

If you want your reader to believe the narrator of your story, it is important to make the narrator sound convincing. One technique a writer can use to create this tone of authority is to use **imperatives**. These are usually a command or an instruction, which tells someone to do something.

Look at this example of how Roald Dahl uses imperatives in *The Witches*.

> Listen very carefully. Never forget what is coming next.

What do you think the effect of these two sentences is? Choose one or more of the options below.

- It makes me want to ignore the narrator.
- It makes me pay attention to what the narrator is about to say.
- It makes me think the narrator is joking.
- It makes me laugh at the narrator.
- It makes me think the narrator has something important to say and that I should listen to him.

How can I make the unbelievable sound believable?

Noun phrases are often used to identify and describe the characters in a story. A writer can choose how much detail to add around their noun phrase.

Why do you think Roald Dahl uses the noun phrase 'REAL WITCHES'? What effect does this create?

Writers can also choose to emphasise ideas by using **repetition**. The noun phrase 'REAL WITCHES' is repeated three times. What effect do you think the writer is trying to achieve here? Can you find any other examples of repetition in the extract?

Activity 2

Re-read the extract below from the opening of *The Witches*.

In fairy-tales, witches always wear silly black hats and black cloaks, and they ride on broomsticks.

But this is not a fairy-tale. This is about REAL WITCHES.

The most important thing you should know about REAL WITCHES is this. Listen very carefully. Never forget what is coming next.

REAL WITCHES dress in ordinary clothes and look very much like ordinary women. They live in ordinary houses and they work in ORDINARY JOBS.

That is why they are hard to catch.

A REAL WITCH hates children with a red-hot sizzling hatred that is more sizzling and red-hot than any hatred you could possibly imagine.

1 Rewrite the extract from *The Witches* to make the narrator sound less authoritative. You could think about changing the imperatives and/or the repetition of noun phrases.

2 Highlight two changes you have made and write two sentences explaining what the change is and the effect it has on your text.

What do better writers do?

Better writers encourage the reader to believe in the story that they are telling, by using devices such as repetition of noun phrases and imperatives to create a tone of authority.

Activity 3

Look at the opening to the following fairy tale:

Once upon a time there was a man and his wife who had the bad luck to live next door to a witch. They longed to have a child, and at last their wish was granted.

One day, the wife had a craving for wild garlic, called Rapunzel, growing in the witch's garden. Her husband picked some for her and she ate it. The next day he went back for more. And on the third… the witch pounced on him!

Try to rewrite this opening so that it sounds less make-believe. Use the questions below to help you think about how to create a sense of authority in your writing so the reader believes that the events that you are relaying actually happened.

- How can I make my writing seem real?
- What choices can I make to create the narrator's tone of authority?

CHECK YOUR WRITING

→ Look at your writing and highlight and comment upon the choices that you have made. It might look something like this:

Let me tell you about some friends of mine. Ella and Tom were a lovely couple who wanted a baby. They lived in a rather average house, on an average street. Their next door neighbour was not average, nor was she lovely; in fact she was an unpleasant woman who hated most people, particularly her neighbours.

The **imperative** creates a tone of authority.

Suggests you know the couple, which makes them seem more real.

Gives the couple names and refers to the witch as a neighbour and an unpleasant woman to make them all seem ordinary.

Repeats the adjective 'average' in noun phrases to suggest how normal these people and their surroundings are, which makes it more believable.

3 Creating vivid images

Learning objective

- Understand how to use verbs to create a vivid image in the reader's mind

Fairy tales and children's literature are full of characters with alter egos, which allow characters to enter alternative worlds. Describing and creating a vivid image of these characters in the reader's mind is crucial to readers enjoying the story.

Activity 1

Read this extract from *Queen* by David Grant. In the story, a girl called Rosie dreams that she becomes Queen of Wolves; she becomes her alter ego.

> When she woke, she was surprised to find she was not in her bedroom. She was outside in the dark night, lying on a carpet of leaves, amongst dark trees. The flames of a fire flickered and, around her, the green eyes of wolves burned in the darkness.
>
> The wolves crept closer into the circle of firelight. The biggest wolf threw back its head and howled for joy. The other wolves circled around her and their yellow teeth clattered as they snapped their drooling jaws and thought of the meal they would have.
>
> Rose pulled her red cape tightly around her shivering shoulders and stood up and made herself as tall as she could and tried to speak without shaking.
>
> "Who do you wolves think you are? Why do you not bow down to your queen?" she said.

1   What images are created in your mind of the wolves? Write down a few words to describe what they look and sound like.

2   How do you think the writer wants the reader to feel about the wolves? Make a note of what you would say or do ifyou met them.

3   What kind of reader do you think this is written for? How can you tell?

WRITER'S WORKSHOP: Creating a vivid image

How can I use language to create vivid description?

Good writers paint a picture in their readers' minds through the language they use. Really good writers choose their verbs carefully to add to this picture.

Look at some of the verbs used in the extract from *Queen*.

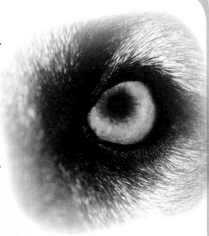

> The flames of a fire flickered and, around her, the green eyes of wolves (burned) in the darkness.
>
> The wolves (crept) closer into the circle of firelight. The biggest wolf (threw) back its head and (howled) for joy. The other wolves (circled) around her and their yellow teeth (clattered) as they (snapped) their drooling jaws and thought of the meal they would have.

Why has the writer chosen these verbs, do you think? What image do they create in your mind of the wolves?

Now look at the alternative example below, where different decisions have been made about the verbs used.

> The flames of a fire flickered and, around her, the green eyes of wolves (sparkled) in the darkness.
>
> The wolves (tip-toed) closer into the circle of firelight. The biggest wolf (tipped) back its head and (whined) for joy. The other wolves (wandered) around her and their yellow teeth (clattered) as they (chomped) their drooling jaws and thought of the meal they would have.

Try rewriting the extract yourself to create a different effect altogether. For example, you might want to make the wolves seem:

- friendly
- funny
- frightened (rather than frightening).

Think about your verb choice here but also feel free to change other words if you wish, to add to the effect.

Activity 2

Write one or two sentences describing a dangerous animal (either real or imaginary). Use the questions below to help you.

- What does my animal look like?
- What features make it frightening?
- How can I use verbs to create a picture of a dangerous animal in the reader's mind?

What do better writers do?

Better writers:

- are aware of the effect they want to have on their reader
- choose verbs carefully in order to paint a picture in their reader's mind.

CHECK YOUR WRITING

➡ Look back at your writing from Activity 2. Annotate your extract to explain some of the decisions you have made. It might look something like this:

Rising up on its enormous hind legs, it towered above the other animals. Briefly, it scanned the ground below. The creature then reared its ugly head and roared.

Verbs indicate the size of the creature which makes it seem threatening.

Verbs used to describe the creature's other movements and the sound it makes, all suggest its power.

4 Describing a transformation

Learning objective

- Understand how to use noun phrases to add descriptive detail

Characters with alter egos often undergo strange transformations. Writers choose their words and phrases carefully to describe these transformations to the reader.

Activity 1

1 Remind yourself of the fictional characters and their alter egos that you listed in Lesson 1. What types of transformation did the characters undergo to change into their alter egos?

2 Think back to the alter ego that you described in Lesson 1. How do you think they might transform into their alter ego?

Activity 2

Read the extract below. It is the opening to Kafka's *Metamorphosis*.

When Gregor Samsa awoke one morning from troubled dreams, he found himself changed into a monstrous cockroach in his bed. He lay on his tough, armoured back, and, raising his head a little, managed to see – sectioned off by his little crescent-shaped ridges into segments – the expanse of his arched, brown belly, atop which the coverlet perched, forever on the point of slipping off entirely. His numerous legs, pathetically frail by contrast to the rest of him, waved feebly before his eyes.

'What's the matter with me?' he thought. It was no dream.

KAFKA
metamorphosis & Other Stories

'One of the greatest writers of the twentieth century' *Guardian*

MODERN CLASSICS

1   What has happened to the main character in this extract?

2   Look at this extract again:

> When Gregor Samsa awoke one morning from troubled dreams,

   a   Why do you think Kafka describes George's dreams as 'troubled'? How does this link to what follows?
   b   How do you think you would feel if you woke up as Gregor has done on this morning?
   c   How do you think the narrator feels about the events he is describing?

WRITER'S WORKSHOP: Describing a transformation

How can I choose descriptive noun phrases?

Writers can add detail through their use of noun phrases.
Look at the choices the author of *Metamorphosis* has made:

troubled dreams   tough, armoured back

little crescent-shaped ridges   numerous legs

arched, brown belly

Why has the author chosen these noun phrases? What
impression do they give to the reader of Gregor's
transformation?

How can I use language to describe what my character has transformed into?

Characters often undergo surprising and instant transformations into their alter ego. Writers make careful language choices to give detailed, graphic descriptions of what their characters have changed into.

- The author chooses the noun 'cockroach'. How is this more descriptive than if the author had chosen a different noun, such as 'bug' or 'insect'?

  The author **pre-modifies** the noun with an adjective: 'a **monstrous** cockroach'. What effect does this have on you as a reader?

Look at the very simple noun phrase below.

> The animal

> a Change the noun 'animal' to something which creates a more negative image in the reader's mind.

> The tarantula

> b Pre-modify the noun with one adjective, to create a strong visual image of the creature (it might be about physical description (e.g. hairy, speckled) or to get the reader to think about the noun more (e.g. terrifying, ordinary). For example:

> the formidable/gigantic/deadly tarantula

Good writers also **post-modify** their noun phrases. This means adding more detail after the noun phrase. One way of doing this is by using a **prepositional phrase**. Look at this example from *Metamorphosis*:

> the expanse **of his arched**, **brown belly**

Why do you think this detail is important?

Look again at the noun phrase that you just created and try to post-modify the noun with a prepositional phrase to add more detail. For example:

> the deadly tarantula with long hairy legs

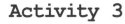

Activity 3

1 Imagine that you wake up in the morning and have been transformed into something gruesome. It can be anything you wish – let your imagination run wild!

   a Note down some nouns and **articles** which describe the thing that you have been transformed into.

   b Pre-modify some nouns with an adjective which suggests what the reader should think or feel about this creature.

   c Add a prepositional phrase which makes your description as vivid as possible.

Articles	Adjectives	Nouns	Prepositional phrases
an	incredible	creature	with its fangs bared

2 Highlight the noun phrases in your word bank which you think really help to create a vivid description of the thing you have transformed into.

3 Using the highlighted phrases, write a short description of the thing that you have suddenly been transformed into.

Before you start writing:

• decide exactly what you want your reader to see

• carefully choose vocabulary which will help to paint this picture.

CHECK YOUR WRITING

➡ Look back at the description of your transformation into something gruesome that you wrote in Activity 3 and highlight and explain how you have used the following to make your description more vivid:

• noun phrases

• pre-modification of nouns with careful choice of adjective(s)

• use of prepositional phrase(s).

Do these create a vivid picture of the transformation?

Make any changes that you feel would help to further describe the transformation to the reader.

5 Narrative viewpoint

Learning objectives

- Understand how narrative viewpoint can affect the reader's response to a text
- Understand how to apply narrative viewpoint to your own writing

Writers need to decide who will narrate their story and from whose point of view the story will be told – this is called narrative viewpoint.

Activity 1

Look again at the extract from *Metamorphosis*.

When Gregor Samsa awoke one morning from troubled dreams, he found himself changed into a monstrous cockroach in his bed. He lay on his tough, armoured back, and, raising his head a little, managed to see – sectioned off by his little crescent-shaped ridges into segments – the expanse of his arched, brown belly, atop which the coverlet perched, forever on the point of slipping off entirely. His numerous legs, pathetically frail by contrast to the rest of him, waved feebly before his eyes.

'What's the matter with me?' he thought. It was no dream.

1 Whose viewpoint is this told from?

2 What choices might the writer have made about whose viewpoint the story is told from? Add your ideas to this list:

> • *The writer could have told this from the viewpoint of Gregor's father discovering him transformed into a cockroach.*

3 The narrator writes in an almost matter of fact way about an extraordinary event. What effect does this have on the reader?

WRITER'S WORKSHOP: Deciding on narrative viewpoint

Before a writer starts writing their story they must decide who will narrate it – the 'eyes' and 'voice' through which the story is told. This is called the **narrative viewpoint**. This can change as the story goes along.

Do I want my story to be told from one person's viewpoint?

A story can be told from the point of view of the main character who is directly involved in the action. 'I' and 'we' are used. This is called **first-person narrative**.

Here is another extract from *The Witches*.

> I myself had two separate encounters with witches before I was eight years old. From the first I escaped unharmed, but on the second occasion I was not so lucky. Things happened to me that will probably make you scream when you read about them. That can't be helped. The truth must be told.

Here we are told everything that happens in the story from the point of view of a character involved in the story, using the pronoun 'I'. The narrator directly addresses the reader, using the second person pronoun 'you'.

Choosing to write in first-person narrative means:

- the writer can describe the main character's thoughts and feelings directly
- the reader might be more engaged because the story is told by someone who was there.

What might some of the limitations of using a first-person narrative be?

Do I want my story to be told by a narrator who is not involved in the story?

A story can also be told from the viewpoint of someone who is not immediately involved but who is observing the action. The pronouns 'he', 'she' and 'they' are used. This is called **third-person narrative**.

Metamorphosis is written in the third person. The author is omniscient (all knowing). He knows what the characters are thinking and comments upon it in the third person, for example:

'What's the matter with me?" he thought. It was no dream.

Writing in the third person means:

* the writer can describe different characters' thoughts and feelings
* the writer can describe events that the main character does not see or hear.

Why do you think the author of *Metamorphosis* chose to write in third-person narrative? What effect does this have on the reader? How would this extract be different if it was written as if told to us directly by Gregor?

Activity 2

Imagine you are the author of *Metamorphosis* and you are experimenting with how you will use narrative viewpoint to describe Gregor's transformation. Write one or two paragraphs in the first person, from a viewpoint of your choice, describing the moment Gregor transforms into a cockroach.

Before you begin, think about:

* the narrative viewpoint that you will use and the impact that this will have on the reader
* how you want the reader to react. Do you want them to be frightened, appalled, shocked, symapathetic? Choose vocabulary carefully to achieve your intended reader response.

What do better writers do?

Better writers think about the advantages and disadvantages of first-person and third-person narrative and choose the viewpoint that best suits the story they want to tell and the effect they want to have on the reader.

CHECK YOUR WRITING

Look back at your writing and consider the following questions.

* Have I effectively described the narrator's reaction to the transformation?
* Have I chosen a narrative viewpoint that has an impact on the reader? Does it have the effect intended?

Which column in the table below best describes your use of narrative viewpoint?

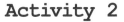

I tried to show a viewpoint in my writing but I didn't do it all the way through.	I used a straightforward viewpoint which I kept throughout my writing.	I developed my ideas well and established a clear viewpoint, adding detail.

6 Adding emphasis

Learning objectives

- Understand how synonyms and intensifiers can be used to add emphasis to writing, creating a grotesque image
- Understand how synonyms can be used to add different layers of meaning

Describing in vivid detail how a character transforms into their alter ego is a crucial skill that writers use to engage and shock their reader. Often, they want to give the reader a detailed description of this. Good writers often choose their language to emphasise or intensify particular ideas or descriptions.

Activity 1

Look at the words below.

frightening

crumpled   foul

putrid   rotting   ghastly   worm-eaten

shrunken   fearsome   decayed   shrivelled

maggots   frightful   cankered   wizened   horror

1   Are any of these words similar in meaning? Group any words with similar meaning together into 'families'. For example:

Reduced in size	Decomposing	Terrifying		
shrunken	rotting			

You can make up some more categories and put the same words into different 'families'.

2   What image do these words create in your mind?

3   Lots of these words are **synonyms** (words that mean the same thing). Why do you think the writer has used lots of synonyms?

4   Can you think of any more synonyms to add to the ones listed above?

5   Write a sentence or two using your own synonyms to describe something grotesque.

Activity 2

Read the extract below. It is from *The Witches* and describes
the Grand High Witch's transformation from a 'pretty lady'
into her alter ego, a grotesque looking witch.

Very slowly, the young lady on the platform raised her hands to her face. I saw her
gloved fingers unhooking something behind her ears, and then… then she caught
hold of her cheeks and lifted her face clean away! The whole of that pretty face came
away in her hands!

It was a mask!

As she took off the mask, she turned sideways and placed it carefully upon a
small table near by, and when she turned round again and faced us, I very nearly
screamed out loud.

That face of hers was the most frightful and frightening thing I have ever seen.
Just looking at it gave me the shakes all over. It was so crumpled and wizened, so
shrunken and shrivelled, it looked as though it had been pickled in vinegar. It was a
fearsome and ghastly sight. There was something terribly wrong with it, something
foul and putrid and decayed. It seemed quite literally to be rotting away at the edges,
and in the middle of the face, around the mouth and cheeks, I could see the skin
all cankered and worm-eaten, as though
maggots were working away in there.

There are times when something is
so frightful you become mesmerized by
it and can't look away. I was like that
now. I was transfixed. I was numbed. I
was magnetized by the sheer horror of
this woman's features. But there was
more to it than that. There was a look
of serpents in those eyes of hers as they
flashed around the audience.

1 How does the narrator feel when the young
lady takes off the mask?

2 What impression do you get of the witch's
appearance? Which words or phrases help
paint this picture in your mind?

WRITER'S WORKSHOP: Emphasising ideas

How do I choose language to add emphasis to my writing?

Synonyms are different words that have the same or very similar meaning. For example, a synonym of the word 'frightening' might be 'terrifying', or a synonym of the word 'pretty' might be 'attractive'.

Writers might use synonyms and related words in three different ways:

- to emphasise particular ideas or details
- to avoid repeating the same word
- to introduce different layers of meaning or detail.

Roald Dahl uses synonyms and related words for heightened impact to describe the transformation of the Grand High Witch's face.

It was so crumpled and wizened,

Look at this student's commentary on the example from *The Witches*.

By using the words 'crumpled and wizened' the author emphasises the idea that the witch has an aged, ugly face. While the words are similar in meaning, 'crumpled' suggests the face has been squashed up or hit by something, and 'wizened' suggests the face is dried up and old looking. The synonyms help to intensify the image we have of the witch's old and unpleasant face.

Choose another pair of synonyms or related words from the extract, such as 'shrunken and shrivelled'. What effect does the pair of words create? In what ways do the related words introduce different layers of meaning?

How can I use intensifiers for effect in my writing?

Writers can use **intensifiers** (or adverbs of degree) to add further emphasis to their ideas. As the name suggests, this intensifies and adds more emphasis to the meaning of a word or phrase.

Common intensifiers include: so   very   really   quite

Look at how Roald Dahl uses intensifiers to describe the Grand High Witch:

so crumpled and wizened, so shrunken and shrivelled … so frightful

Adverbs ending in -ly are often used as intensifiers: There was something terribly wrong with it…

Remove the intensifiers from the extract. How does this alter the impact on the reader? Do you prefer the version with or without the intensifiers?

Rewrite your sentences from Activity 1, using some of the intensifiers listed above and choosing new ones.

Does your use of intensifiers change the impact or meaning of the sentences? How much is enough – or too much!

Activity 3

Imagine that one of your teachers removes a mask from his/her face in one of your lessons to reveal something truly horrible underneath or imagine that a very ugly teacher takes off his/her mask to reveal an incredibly beautiful face underneath.

1 Write down some synonyms which describe what you have just seen. Highlight the ones that you think are the most effective.

2 Add some intensifiers to your synonyms for emphasis but use them sparingly, otherwise they will lose their impact.

3 Write a few sentences describing what lies behind the mask of your teacher. Before you start writing think about:

- what effect you want to have on your reader
- choosing your language carefully and adding emphasis where you think it is necessary.

What do better writers do?

Better writers:

- use synonyms to emphasise ideas and details in their story and to avoid repetition – they choose these synonyms carefully to introduce different layers of meaning

- know when to use intensifiers to add further emphasis to a word or phrase, but do not overuse them.

CHECK YOUR WRITING

Look back at your writing from Activity 3. Annotate your extract to explain some of the decisions you have made. It might look something like this:

Beneath the mask lay such *horror. The face was* so repulsive, so repellent, so *evil. It had two empty eye sockets. The empty holes seemed to move in the darkness beneath the mask. They were filled with worms, which* slithered, slipped *and* slid.

Synonyms emphasise the horror of the sight and the fear that it creates.

Intensifiers heighten the revulsion and terror that the narrator feels towards the thing.

Are there any changes that you can make to your writing to make it seem even more grotesque and frightening?

Assessment: Transformation

Learning objective

- Understand how to craft a short story extract using a range of features for effect

PLAN

Follow the steps below to collect your ideas and make important decisions before you start writing. You can use the ideas you have generated in previous lessons.

1 What kind of overall effect are you hoping to achieve? How do you want your readers to react to this part of the story? Should they feel:

So far in this unit, you have explored:

- the concept of an alter ego
- creating different alter egos
- creating a tone of authority in your writing through careful use of noun phrases
- carefully choosing detail to describe a transformation
- choosing a narrative viewpoint to suit your story
- selecting verbs and other vocabulary which paint a vivid picture in your reader's mind
- using synonyms and intensifiers to emphasise details in your writing.

You will use all the skills that you have developed to craft a short story extract which describes the transformation of a character into his/her alter ego.

Nervous?   Terrified?   Excited?   Amused?   Tense?

2 Who is my character? Consider what your character is like before their transformation.

Male or female?   Age?   Are they likeable?   Think of their key characteristics. What do they look like?

Do they have a job or perhaps go to school?

3 What type of transformation will they undergo?

Will it be painful or painless?

Will it be shocking, gruesome, painful or perhaps even funny?   Will the change be sudden or gradual?   What will it look like?

4 How will my character feel about their transformation?

Pleased?   Horrified?   Shocked?   Confused?   Agitated?

5 Where will the transformation take place?

Will your character be on their own?   In a laboratory, bedroom or somewhere else?   In a public setting like a classroom or shop?

6 What narrative viewpoint will I use?

First person from your character's point of view?   First person from the alter ego's point of view?

Third-person omniscient narrator?   Third-person narrator who is a friend or family member involved in the action?

WRITE

You are now ready to write. Write a short extract in which you describe the transformation of your character into his/her alter ego. Aim to write between 150 and 200 words.

REFLECT

1 When you have completed your extract, read it through carefully.

a Are you pleased with it? Which of the following do you feel you have achieved?

b Choose one or two areas where you think you have made effective choices. Briefly explain why you made these choices and what effect you think they create.

c Now do the same for one or two areas where you think you might be able to improve your writing. Improve and annotate or edit your piece with the above in mind.

☐ I think I have chosen the most effective narrative viewpoint for this extract.

☐ I think I make choices that make this transformation sound realistic.

☐ I think my choice of verbs adds effective detail to my description of the transformation.

☐ I think my use of noun phrases helps me describe the character and his/her transformation effectively.

☐ I think I have chosen when to use synonyms and other vocabulary choices to emphasise and intensify details of my writing.

☐ I think my writing will have the impact I want it to have on the reader.

CHECK YOUR WRITING

⬇ Looking at the table below, decide which column you think best describes the writing you crafted in this assessment:

I tried to show a viewpoint in my writing but I didn't always do that all the way through it.	I used a straightforward viewpoint which I kept throughout my writing.	I used a clear viewpoint which was suitable for my story.
I chose some effective nouns and verbs to describe the transformation of my character.	I chose some noun and verb phrases deliberately to describe the transformation of my character.	I chose noun and verb phrases deliberately to create the impression I wanted my reader to have of my transformation.
I tried to create a picture in my reader's mind through my description.	I painted a picture in my reader's mind using some imaginative detail.	I tried to engage my reader by creating a vivid picture in their mind of the transformation by using lots of imaginative detail.

7 Creating immediacy

Learning objectives

- Understand how present participles can be used to create a sense of immediacy
- Understand how verb choice can be used to convey action

Alter egos can come in any form – even vampires. Stories about vampires are very popular and the writers of these stories want to keep their readers reading. They often achieve this by creating a sense of immediacy in their narratives.

Activity 1

Look at this passage from *Cirque du Freak*, which describes how Darren Shan briefly transforms into his vampire alter ego.

> I walked around the back of her, my hands never leaving her flesh. I could feel the veins throbbing as I stroked them, and when I pressed down on one near the bottom of her neck, I could see it standing out, blue and beautiful, begging to be ripped open and sucked dry.
> I bared my teeth and leaned forward, jaws wide open.

1   How does Darren react to his sister Annie in this passage?
2   Which one word suggests the character sees the girl as a piece of meat to be devoured?
3   Consider how the author wants us to feel about the narrator here. How is this achieved?
4   What do you think might happen next? Consider the following and note down your ideas.
  - Will she (Annie) see him? How will she react to her brother turned vampire?
  - Will Darren's alter ego actually bite her? What will happen then?
  - Or will something happen to stop him? What or who will this be?

WRITER'S WORKSHOP: Conveying immediacy and action

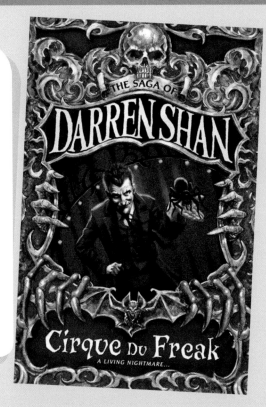

How can I use language to create a sense of immediacy?

Writers often try to engage the reader in the story by creating a sense of immediacy. This can be achieved by using **present participles**, which suggest that the action is happening as we read.

Look at how present participles have been used in the extract below.

> I walked around the back of her, my hands never (leaving) her flesh. I could feel the veins (throbbing) as I stroked them, and when I pressed down on one near the bottom of her neck, I could see it (standing) out, blue and beautiful, (begging) to be ripped open and sucked dry.

Who or what do these present participles refer to? How effective are these words in showing the reader what is happening?

How can I use language to convey action?

Writers can convey the action in their narratives through their careful use of verbs which can help to heighten the tension in their writing.

Look again at the extract. This time the past tense verbs have been highlighted:

> I walked around the back of her, my hands never leaving her flesh. I could feel the veins throbbing as I stroked them, and when I pressed down on one near the bottom of her neck, I could see it standing out, blue and beautiful, begging to be ripped open and sucked dry. I bared my teeth and leaned forward, jaws wide open.

Whose actions do these verbs refer to?

Why do you think the writer has used past tense verbs in the same paragraph as the present participles? What effect does this create?

Activity 2

1 Look at the predictions that you made in Activity 1, question 4. You are now going to use these ideas to help you continue the extract from *Cirque du Freak*.

   Before you start writing think about:

   - exactly what will happen next
   - how you want your reader to respond to your writing
   - noting down some present participles which will help to create a sense of immediacy so that your reader is continually waiting to see what happens next
   - noting down some verbs which help to convey the action.

2 Using all your ideas from above write the next one or two paragraphs which describe what happens next to Darren Shan's alter ego and to his sister Annie. Remember to create a sense of immediacy through your use of present participles.

CHECK YOUR WRITING

→ Look back at the extract you have just written and annotate it. Highlight the following and explain how you have used them to create a particular effect:

   - use of present participles to create immediacy
   - other verb choices which convey action.

↓ Look at the table below and see which column best describes your writing.

I tried to create a sense of immediacy through using some present participles and I began to convey some sense of action through my verb choice.	I created a sense of immediacy through my use of present participles and conveyed some sense of action through my verb choice.	I created and sustained a strong sense of immediacy through my use of present participles and conveyed action through my verb choice.

8 Creating a split identity

Learning objective

- Understand how writers use narrative voice to create a sense of split identity

Writers create split identities when writing about alter egos and they often achieve this through their use of narrative voice.

Narrative voice is how the 'speaker' of the story sounds – the distinctive tone of the storytelling.

Activity 1

Look at this section of the text from *Cirque du Freak*, which describes how Darren Shan reacts to his sister and to his own alter ego.

I walked around the back of her, my hands never leaving her flesh. I could feel the veins throbbing as I stroked them, and when I pressed down on one near the bottom of her neck, I could see it standing out, blue and beautiful, begging to be ripped open and sucked dry.

I bared my teeth and leaned forward, jaws wide open.

At the last moment, as my lips touched her neck, I caught sight of my reflection in the mirror and thankfully that was enough to make me pause.

The face in the mirror was a twisted, unfamiliar mask, full of red eyes, sharp wrinkles and a vicious grin. I lifted my head for a closer look. It was me but at the same time it wasn't. It was like there were two people sharing one body, a normal human boy and a savage animal of the night.

As I stared, the ugly face faded and the urge to drink blood passed. I gazed at Annie, horrified. I'd been about to *bite* her! I would have *fed* on my own sister!

I fell away from her with a cry and covered my face with my hands, afraid of the mirror and what I might see. Annie staggered backwards, then looked around at the bathroom in a dazed kind of way.

1 Were your predictions about what might happen right?

2 Do you prefer your own predictions or the choice that the author made? Why?

3 Which two noun phrases describe the boy and his alter ego?

WRITER'S WORKSHOP: Bringing an alter ego to life

How can I use a shift in narrative voice to make an alter ego come to life?

Writers can change narrative voice in order to offer a different perspective. In some stories there can be different speakers who tell the story, which adds variety and invites the reader to view the events from different angles.

In the extract from *Cirque du Freak* there is a shift in narrative voice. Look at the extract again. Which text is from the vampire's perspective and which is from the boy's perspective?

What is it that makes him shift his perspective from his alter ego back to his 'real' self? What do you notice about how the narrative voice changes?

Do you think this extract is effective in portraying a split identity? Why?

Activity 2

1 Think about the alter ego that you have created in previous lessons. Imagine what kind of narrative voice they might have. Consider the following questions.

- How will they speak and sound?
- Do you want your reader to like/dislike/trust/distrust them?

Briefly describe the narrative voice that you would use.

2 Think of something that could happen to make the other self (your original character) view his/her alter ego, undergoing an inner crisis. Use this point to switch the narrative voice to show the split identity. Your alter ego might:

- see a reflection of him/herself
- have an out of body experience and look at other self as an observer
- see the response of a friend/relative and suddenly see themselves as they see them
- catch a glimpse of their other self on CCTV.

3 Consider the impact that you want this shift in narrative voice to have. Write a paragraph which shows the point at which the crisis peaks and the voice changes.

CHECK YOUR WRITING

→ Look back at the extract you have just written and annotate it. Highlight the techniques that you have used. It might look something like this:

→ Write a couple of sentences explaining how you have demonstrated a shift in narrative voice and what impact this has on the reader.

Preparing to pounce on my prey, I glanced up. A CCTV image loomed above me. Stunned and shocked, I found myself reeling back. What was this creature? The grainy image showed me what I had not seen, what I had refused to accept until now.

Shift in narrative voice from the alter ego who is ready to 'pounce' on 'her' 'prey' to the narrator who has seen herself on CCTV and wonders what 'this creature' is, revealing the split identity.

9 Building detail

Learning objectives

- Understand how to elaborate simple sentences to provide narrative description
- Understand how to use short sentences for dramatic impact

Writers try to build up as much detail as they can about setting, characters and events in their sentences. They also often use short, **simple sentences** for dramatic impact in their stories.

Activity 1

Look at how the following simple sentences are used. They are from an extract in a previous lesson from *The Witches* describing the Grand Witch's transformation.

> Very slowly, the young lady on the platform raised her hands to her face
> [...] The whole of that pretty face came away in her hands! It was a mask!

1 What do you notice about the final sentence in contrast with the previous two sentences? What is the effect of this?

2 What is the effect of the adjectives 'young' and 'pretty' which are used to describe the witch's other self?

3 Look at the beginning of the first sentence. Why do you think Roald Dahl has chosen to begin it with the **adverbial phrase** 'Very slowly'? Try changing the word order by reordering the phrases and see what impact this has on the sentence.

| The young lady | on the platform | raised her hands |
| very slowly | to her face. | |

4 What important details do the adverbial phrases 'very slowly' and 'to her face' reveal?

WRITER'S WORKSHOP: Building detail/creating impact

How do I build detail into simple sentences?

A simple sentence doesn't have to be simple. It can reveal lots of information and can be manipulated to achieve various effects. This is an example from *Cirque du Freak* of a simple sentence that has been elaborated by the author by adding detail:

> With one angry gesture, I swallowed the contents of the bottle.

A simple sentence has only one clause, or is a main clause. A clause is a group of words including a verb. So the writer might have started with the sentence:

> I swallowed the contents.

They might then have expanded the noun phrase:

> I swallowed the contents of the bottle.

Detail can then be added to make it more interesting, for example:

- by using an adverbial phrase to say **how** he swallowed it

> With one gesture, I swallowed the contents of the bottle.

- by using adjective(s) to describe **what** the gesture was like

> With one angry gesture, I swallowed the contents of the bottle.

- by using an adverb to say **when** he swallowed the contents of the bottle.

> Suddenly, with one angry gesture, I swallowed the contents of the bottle.

Write a simple sentence and try to elaborate it in this way. Consider which version of your sentence you prefer. Would you always want to add this much detail to every sentence?

How do I use simple sentences to create dramatic impact?

Simple sentences can also be very short and just as effective. Writers often use short sentences for dramatic impact.

Look at the last sentence from the extract on page 26:

> 'It was a mask!'

Why has Roald Dahl used a short simple sentence here? Do you think it is effective?

As you can see from the examples above, simple sentences can be far from simple and writers manipulate them to create different effects.

Activity 2

Below are some images which depict people in a moment of crisis. You will need to imagine in more detail what this crisis is. Pick one of these pictures to describe.

<table>
</table>

What do better writers do?

Better writers:

- add detail to a simple sentence by carefully selecting adverbs, adverbial phrases, adjectives and by expanding noun phrases
- use a short, simple sentence for a key moment in the plot.

Before you begin writing think about how you want your reader to feel and/or think at this moment in crisis. Now answer the questions below.

1   Write a paragraph of about five sentences to communicate the build up to this crisis.

2   Then write a very short sentence to help emphasise a key moment, feeling or fact in the crisis. It should help to heighten the dramatic impact of the moment that you are describing.

See the example below and consider how the short, simple sentences are used to describe the character's desperation to breathe which heightens his feelings of panic as he drowns.

This time he is underwater, running, feet sinking deeper and deeper into the bed. The surface is within his reach if he raises his arms, but he can't get his head out of the water. **He has to breathe. The compulsion to inhale is huge**. But he can't, he musn't.

Try and use a similar technique in your own writing.

3 Now consider whether any of your sentences might be effective as a more elaborated simple sentence. See the prompts below to help you to elaborate your sentence.

- Choose different nouns or noun phrases.
- Show more by using adjectives.
- Add more information with adverbs or adverbial phrases (words or phrases that tell you **when**, **where** or **how** something happens).

CHECK YOUR WRITING

Now look at your own use of simple sentences. Which ones do you think are most effective at:

- building up detail to describe setting, character and events
- heightening the dramatic impact?

Explain your reasons in one or two sentences.

10 Tension and pace

Learning objectives

- Understand how short sentences emphasise the tense moments in a narrative
- Understand how sentence length can be used to suggest pace in a narrative

Writers vary sentence length to build up tension and pace in their writing.

Activity 1

Read the following passage which describes a climactic moment in *Cirque du Freak*. A deadly poisonous spider, called Madame Octa, that Darren has stolen from a vampire and tried to tame, bites his friend Steve when they are disturbed by Darren's sister Annie.

> She saw Steve and the monstrous spider on his shoulder, its fangs glinting as though getting ready to bite, and she did the natural thing.
>   She screamed.
>   The sound alarmed me. My head turned, the flute slid from my lips, and my concentration snapped. My link to Madam Octa disintegrated. She shook her head, took a couple of quick steps closer to Steve's throat, then bared her fangs and appeared to grin.
>   Steve roared with fear and surged to his feet. He swiped at the spider, but she ducked and his hand missed. Before he could try again, Madam Octa lowered her head, quick as a snake, *and sank her poison-tipped fangs into his neck*!

1 How does the narrator make the spider seem terrifying?

2 Look at these short simple sentences:

   She screamed.   The sound alarmed me.   My link to Madam Octa disintegrated.

   What is effective about these? Why has the writer used them?

3 Why do you think 'She screamed.' is written as one paragraph?

WRITER'S WORKSHOP: Varying your sentences

How do I vary my sentence length to build up tension?

Read the extract aloud. How would the impact of the sentences 'She screamed. The sound alarmed me.' be altered if they were one longer sentence like the ones below, rather than two short sentences?

She screamed and the sound alarmed me.

When she screamed, the sound alarmed me.

Short sentences tend to create a short stop in the text which emphasises the information in that sentence.

How can I use longer sentences to create pace?

Read the extract aloud again. This time, think about the rhythm of the sentences as you read them. Listen for the way the short sentences create a tiny moment of pause, but listen also for the flow of the longer sentences. If you were reading this extract aloud to someone else, which sentences would you want to read faster as the action builds up?

Look at the sentence below:

She shook her head, took a couple of quick steps closer to Steve's throat, then bared her fangs and appeared to grin.

What difference would it make to the rhythm and pace of the writing if it was written as four short simple sentences?

She shook her head. She took a couple of quick steps closer to Steve's throat. She then bared her fangs. She appeared to grin.

Which example do you think is the most effective at creating pace? Why?

Now look at the sentence the author uses to describe Steve's reaction:

He swiped at the spider, but she ducked and his hand missed.

How could you alter this sentence to change the pace of the last paragraph?

What do better writers do?

Better writers vary their sentence length to build up tension and create pace.

31

Activity 2

The following extract describes Flip dreaming that he is drowning. He is a boy who has woken up
in someone else's body (his alter ego) and can't get out. The situation is nightmarish.

Read the extract and then note down your responses to the questions.

This time he is underwater, running, feet sinking deeper and deeper into the bed. The surface
is within his reach if he raises his arms, but he can't get his head out of the water. He has to
breathe. The compulsion to inhale is huge. But he can't, he mustn't. Still he runs, getting
nowhere, each frantic step burying his feet in the wet sand until he is no longer able to lift
them. Finally, with one great gulp, he opens his mouth, his lungs, to the flood of foul seawater.

Alex woke. Sat up in bed. His heart was racing and he gasped for air as though he'd actually
been drowning.

1   How does Flip feel here? Do you think the author effectively conveys his feelings?

2   Look at the first two sentences. How do they help to create pace?

3   Now look at the following three short sentences:

He has to breathe. The compulsion to inhale is huge. But he can't, he mustn't.

4   What happens to the rhythm of the writing here? Do you think it is effective at conveying
Flip's growing sense of panic?

5   How did you respond to the last three sentences? How do you think the writer uses
sentence length to make you feel like this?

Activity 3

Think about what could happen next to Flip and write the next few sentences describing what you imagine.

Think about how you vary your sentence length to create rhythm and pace.

CHECK YOUR WRITING

⊙ Look back at your writing from Activity 2. Annotate your extract to explain some of the decisions that you have made. It might look something like this:

⬇ Look at the table below and see which column best describes your writing.

He clutched at his throat, still dry and raw. He needed air. Needed it desperately. He tried to keep his growing hysteria from surfacing but it was no use. He began to wheeze, struggling for air, his panic causing his airways to constrict rapidly.

▮ Longer sentences suggest how events are happening in quick succession, increasing the pace and the fear that Flip feels.

▮ Short sentences create dramatic impact as they make the reader pause, highlighting Flip's desperation for air.

I tried to create a sense of pace through my use of longer sentences and at times I created tension through my use of short, simple sentences.	I created pace through my use of longer sentences and I created tension through my use of some short simple sentences.	I created and sustained a clear sense of pace through my use of longer sentences and I heightened the tension of my writing by my use of short, simple sentences.

33

11 Emphasising meaning

Learning objective

- Understand how writers use punctuation to emphasise meaning

Writers use punctuation to emphasise meaning in their writing as well as to clarify and avoid ambiguity.

Activity 1

Look at the following sentence. How many different ways can you punctuate it?

A woman without her man is nothing

How can the punctuation alter the sentence's meaning?

Look at the following two emails.

How does the meaning change in the second email?

reply | reply all | forward | X delete

INBOX

From

To

Subject

Dear Jack

I want a man who knows what love is all about. You are generous, kind, thoughtful. People who are not like you admit to being useless and inferior. You have ruined me for other men. I yearn for you. I have no feelings whatsoever when we're apart. I can be forever happy – will you let me be yours?

Jill

X delete

Subject

Dear Jack

I want a man who knows what love is. All about you are generous, kind, thoughtful people, who are not like you. Admit to being useless and inferior me. For other men I yearn! For you I have no feelings whatsoever. When we're apart I can be forever happy. Will you let me be?

Yours,

Jill

Activity 2

Read this extract from *Twilight*, which describes Bella's close encounter with a car.

I saw several things simultaneously. Nothing was moving in slow motion, the way it does in movies. Instead, the adrenaline rush seemed to make my brain work much faster, and I was able to absorb in clear detail several things at once.

Edward Cullen was standing four cars down from me, staring at me in horror. His face stood out from a sea of faces, all frozen in the same mask of shock. But of more immediate importance was the dark blue van that was skidding, tyres locked and squealing against the brakes, spinning wildly across the ice of the parking lot. It was going to hit the back corner of my truck, and I was standing between them. I didn't even have time to close my eyes.

Just before I heard the shattering crunch of the van folding around the truck bed, something hit me, hard, but not from the direction I was expecting. My head cracked against the icy blacktop, and I felt something solid and cold pinning me to the ground. I was lying on the pavement behind the tan car I'd parked next to. But I didn't have a chance to notice anything else, because the van was still coming. It had curled gratingly around the end of the truck and, still spinning and sliding, was about to collide with me *again*.

A low oath made me aware that someone was with me, and the voice was impossible not to recognise. Two long, white hands shot out protectively in front of me, and the van shuddered to a stop a foot from my face, the large hands fitting providentially into a deep dent in the side of the van's body.

Then his hands moved so fast they blurred. One was suddenly gripping under the body of the van, and something was dragging me, swinging my legs around like a rag doll's, till they hit the tyre of the tan car. A groaning metallic thud hurt my ears, and the van settled, glass popping, onto the asphalt – exactly where, a second ago, my legs had been.

It was absolutely silent for one long second before the screaming began. In the abrupt bedlam, I could hear more than one person shouting my name. But more clearly than all the yelling, I could hear Edward Cullen's low, frantic voice in my ear.

1 How does Edward manage to save Bella?

2 Why is this moment tense and exciting? Can you identify any punctuation that the author uses to achieve this?

3 Do you think the author has used punctuation effectively here? Try to explain your reasons.

35

WRITER'S WORKSHOP: Clever punctuation

How can I use punctuation to clarify?

It can be used to add additional detail. The writer uses parenthetical commas (instead of brackets) to slot in extra information and the information within the commas can always be removed. For example:

> It had curled gratingly around the curve of the truck and, still spinning and sliding, was about to collide with me *again*.

Can you find any more examples of phrases which use parenthetical commas? What effect do you think they have on the writing? Is the extra detail that is added important?

How can I use punctuation to emphasise meaning in my writing?

Punctuation is essential to meaning, helping to add emphasis to certain points in the text. It can mimic the movement described in the text; create tension and drama; add pathos; highlight humour; create tone, and numerous other things. It is absolutely essential to writing!

Look at the sentence below and consider how the writer has used punctuation to create tension. What, for example, is the effect of the dash?

> A groaning metallic thud hurt my ears, and the van settled, glass popping, onto the asphalt – exactly where, a second ago, my legs had been.

How can I use punctuation to keep my reader engaged?

Punctuation is used by writers to engage the reader, keeping them involved in the text. Ellipses (...) can be used to show gaps in a text which can keep the reader guessing, inviting them to fill in the gaps.

Look at how ellipses have been used in the following text. It is the ending to *Cirque du Freak*, describing how Darren walks off with the vampire, Mr Crepsley.

> Then he took my hand in his and grinned bloodthirstily. 'Let us go eat.'
> I took a deep breath and tried not to think about what might be on the menu. I nodded nervously and squeezed his hand. We turned and faced away from the graves. Then, side by side, the vampire and his assistant, we began walking…
> … into the night.
> TO BE CONTINUED…

What is the impact of this ending on the reader?

Ellipses can be used to great effect, but can lose their effect if they are overused. Do you think punctuation has been used effectively here?

Activity 3

1 Look at the piece of writing that you completed in the last lesson. Have you used punctuation to emphasise meaning and heighten the tension?

2 Edit your piece, paying particular attention to your use of punctuation and the impact that you want it to have on the reader.

What do better writers do?

Better writers use punctuation in their writing to aid understanding and to emphasise meaning, for example, to heighten the drama and tension of their narrative.

CHECK YOUR WRITING

Look back at the piece that you edited in Activity 3 and consider which column best describes your use of punctuation.

I used straightforward punctuation such as full stops, capital letters, question marks, commas and exclamation marks in my writing which begin to clarify its meaning.	I accurately demarcated sentences. I used most punctuation accurately and used it to emphasise some points in my writing.	I used a range of punctuation, although I sometimes made errors with difficult structures. I used it to emphasise meaning and created tension in my writing.

12 Creating the crisis

Learning objective

- Understand how to plan the crisis moment of an alter ego story

You are going to write the crisis moment of your alter ego story. Before you start writing you need to plan your ideas, possibly re-using some of the work that you did earlier in the unit, or you might want to begin again.

Activity 1

1 What ingredients make a successful crisis to a story? Think about the climactic moments that you read in the last two lessons and any others that you may have read and make a list.

2 Highlight the ingredients that you would like to include in the climax to your alter ego story.

3 Now you need to think about **what** will happen in this moment, **where** it will happen and **who** it will happen to. Write down your ideas for the 'what', 'where' and 'who' for your crisis moment. You can use the ideas below to help.

WHAT...   You might wish to start with the event:

trapped behind a locked door

chased by a wild, dangerous animal

jumping from a jetty into the turbulent sea beneath

WHERE... You could begin with the setting:

a windswept beach

a deserted playground in a local park

a town square, milling with people

woods, darkening in the twilight

WHO...   You could start with your character:

a creature of the night

a human sized and terrifying spider

an ordinary looking girl who patiently waits for what?

Activity 2

You now need to consider the following before you start writing your crisis piece. Write a sentence or two for each explaining your decision.

1 What effect do I want my writing to have on my reader? How will I achieve this?

2 What narrative viewpoint and narrative voice will I use? Consider whose viewpoint you want to tell the story from. Will you stick with this viewpoint throughout the crisis or will you switch viewpoints?

3 How do I want to depict my alter ego? Think about how you want your reader to respond to him/her/it. Which verbs and noun phrases will you use to describe your character, setting and events and to create an image in your reader's mind?

4 How will I build detail in my sentences and vary my sentence length to create pace and heighten tension? Think about how you will build detail in sentences and use different sentence lengths to create rhythm and pace as well as emphasise key moments.

5 What vocabulary choices will I choose to make my writing exciting and engage my reader? Think about how you might like to create a sense of tension and immediacy, through your use of present participles, or through using intensifiers and synonyms and related words to add emphasis to your writing.

CHECK YOUR PLANNING

Look at the planning for the extract from your story. Will your extract:

- hook your reader in, suspending their sense of disbelief?
- create a clear sense of your alter ego's split identity?
- create a sense of tension and immediacy?
- fulfil the success criteria you highlighted at the beginning of the lesson?

If you answered 'maybe' or 'not sure' or 'no' to any of these questions, consider your plan again and think about how to improve it.

Assessment: Writing a crisis piece

Learning objective

- Understand how to write a crisis piece

WRITE

You are now ready to complete the final task in this unit:

Your task:

Write a short story extract about the crisis that your alter ego undergoes. Aim to write between 400 and 600 words.

Remember to:

- consider the plan you prepared

- use all the skills and knowledge that you have gained and practised in this unit

- craft your writing, thinking carefully about the choices you make at word and sentence level

- engage your reader by suspending their disbelief

REFLECT

1 When you have finished writing the first draft of your story, read it through carefully. Are you pleased with it?

a Look at the following points. Which ones do you think you have achieved?

- ☐ I think I hook the reader in, engaging them in the story.
- ☐ I think I use narrative viewpoint and narrative voice effectively for this story extract.
- ☐ I think I clearly describe the split identity of my protagonist.
- ☐ I think I create a sense of tension and immediacy through my language choices.
- ☐ I think I use a range of sentence lengths to create pace and to build up tension.
- ☐ I think I use punctuation to emphasise meaning.
- ☐ I think I achieve the impact that I intend to have on my reader.

b Find an example from your story extract to support any of the points you feel you have achieved.

2 a Choose one or two areas in your writing which you feel you could improve. This might be:

* improving your language choices, such as:

making more effective use of noun phrases, using language more concisely

or

* varying your use of viewpoint and voice, perhaps using a dual narrative to create a different perspective:

making the telling more varied and exciting.

b Look back at the relevant pages in this unit to remind yourself of the choices and techniques you would use to improve your writing in these one or two areas.

c Re-read some of the exemplar texts that we have looked at, which demonstrate how these techniques are used successfully.

d Think about *how* you will make these changes and then make the improvements to your writing.

CHECK YOUR WRITING

➡ Look at your own writing and using the checklist to guide you, annotate your work in a different colour. Alternatively, write sticky notes explaining what went well and stick them onto your work. It might look something like this:

⬇ Look at the table below and decide which column you think best describes your crisis piece.

A deafening silence surrounded me. Fear caught at my throat, struggling to be heard. I was mute. The frightening stillness continued...

▨ Synonyms and related words used to emphasise the silence

▨ Short simple sentences used for dramatic impact, to increase the tension

▨ Ellipsis used to reflect how the narrator and the reader wait to see what happens next, heightening the tension

Use of first-person narrative engages the reader, making them empathise with the narrator, sharing in her fear.

I planned my writing and wrote my extract sometimes thinking about how I maintained my reader's interest.	I planned my writing and wrote my extract thinking about how I maintained the interest of the reader.	I planned my writing and wrote my extract thinking about how it would hook the reader in and keep them engaged throughout.
I tried to choose some language in my extract for its effect.	I deliberately chose language in my extract for its effect.	I used a wide range of vocabulary for its effect.
I sometimes tried to vary my sentence length for effect.	I tried to create a sense of pace and emphasise some key moments by varying my sentence length.	I created pace and emphasised key moments by varying my sentence length.
I can use straightforward punctuation such as full stops, capital letters, question marks, commas and exclamation marks.	I can use punctuation to make my meaning clear and to sometimes add emphasis to my writing.	I can use a range of punctuation to make my meaning clear and to add emphasis to my writing.

41

Unit 2
Writing the world

In this unit, you will explore how people write about the world of nature. You will look at nature documentaries and campaigns about the environment to understand how nature is described and presented in popular media. You will learn to use language that makes you sound like an expert on the natural world, and that persuades people to take action to protect the environment. Finally, you will be able to use the skills you learn from the texts and activities in this unit to write your own persuasive campaign text.

1 Presenting the natural world

Learning objective

* Understand typical stories and issues in popular films and documentaries about the natural world

Many people are fascinated by the natural world and the animals that live in it. Nature **documentaries** and films about nature are popular with a wide range of people and for a variety of reasons.

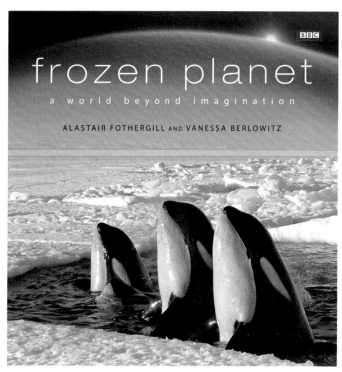

African Cats, *Chimpanzee*, *The Secret Life of Plants*, *The Blue Planet*, *Springwatch*, *Countryfile*... How many films and TV programmes about nature can you name? Why do you think nature documentaries are so popular?

Glossary

documentary: a film or TV programme describing real events with no fictional elements.

Activity 1

1 Look at the list of reasons below about why people watch nature documentaries.

   a Which ones do you most agree with? List them in the order you think is most important.

   b Are there any other reasons why people might watch nature documentaries? Add these to your list.

- The photography is amazing.

- They are entertaining for the whole family.

- They teach you interesting facts about animals and the environment.

- They show how you can protect the environment.

Activity 2

1 Read the extract from an interview with Luc Jacquet, director of *March of the Penguins*, and think about the reasons he gives for making the film.

'I am particularly inspired by the sheer beauty of Antarctica, and I felt this was a great story for the movies – the penguins living on the razor's edge. It's about the struggle between life and death. The penguins live where no other creature can. This is what struck me the most. How do they do it? How do they manage? I wanted to write a story that made the viewer feel like he or she was really right there with the penguins ... to tell things more as I felt them, rather than to describe them as a scientist. In my opinion, the best way to protect the planet is to get people to like it. One protects what one loves. It's obvious that global warming has an impact on the penguins. But we have to find other ways to communicate to people about it, not just lecture them.'

2 Why do you think Luc Jacquet made *March of the Penguins?* Read the list of possible reasons and score each one T (true), F (false) or N (not enough evidence).

a to show people how beautiful Antarctica is

b to make a lot of money

c to make people more aware of the impact of global warming

d to make people cry

e to share his admiration for the way penguins survive.

Activity 3

1 The photograph is a still from a documentary about polar bears affected by global warming.

a Decide which title and blurb best sum up the documentary.

b Write a short paragraph explaining the reasons for your choice.

	Title	Blurb
A	*Save the Bears*	Bears are going to die unless we help them.
B	*Polar Bears in Peril*	Polar bears have ruled the Arctic for 100,000 years, but now they're struggling for survival as the ice around them shrinks.

What do better writers do?

Better writers:

- use titles and blurbs that sum up the nature story or issue in a few words
- use key words that show **what** the story is about, **who** is involved and **where** it happens
- use colourful, powerful words and phrases to attract your attention.

2 Stories from nature

Learning objective

- Understand how titles, taglines and blurbs are used to summarise stories and issues and to attract attention to them

Nature films and TV documentaries often tell powerful stories about survival in the wild. Titles, taglines and blurbs are used to summarise the storyline and make it sound interesting or exciting.

		What effect does it have?
Title	*The Trek of the Wildebeest*	Tells us the main characters in the story. 'Trek' suggests that the wildebeests' journey will be long and difficult, but they are determined to get there.
Tagline	On the plains of Africa, the planet's most epic animal migration is underway.	Tells us the setting for the story and that the migration will be a huge struggle for survival.
Blurb	As the wildebeest slowly mass into a huge single herd, the sound and sight is staggering, a charging mass of energy that stretches from one horizon to the other. Experience a journey like no other on the planet.	Makes the story sound exciting and dramatic. Tells us that vast numbers of animals are taking part in one of the most demanding journeys in the natural world.

Activity 1

1 Look at the film poster for *The Last Roar of the Lions*, a documentary about lions battling for survival in the Okavanga Delta in Africa, as mining companies move in to search for precious metals.

   a What does the image tell you about the story?

   b Using a table like this one, complete the empty boxes.

		What effect does it have?
Title	*The Last Roar of the Lions*	
Tagline	Only the strongest survive.	Tells us that lions are powerful but that they are threatened and in trouble.
Blurb	Majestic and noble, the lion is the most relentless fighter on the planet. But as their lands are threatened by mineral mining, for these big cats every day represents a perilous struggle for survival.	

Activity 2

1 Read the fact file for the film *Polar Bear: Spy on the Ice*.

a Is it a good film title? Write a short paragraph explaining what you think.

b Write a tagline that sums up the story and attracts attention.

c Look back at the blurbs for *The Trek of the Wildebeest* and *The Last Roar of the Lions*. Use them as models to write a blurb for *Polar Bear: Spy on the Ice*. Write two or three sentences that summarise the story and make it sound interesting and exciting.

Fact file

Documentary made in 2011
David Tennant is the narrator
Shot mainly using hidden spy cameras
Gets closer than ever before to polar bears' lives
Shows the struggles they face as their ice-world shrinks

WRITER'S WORKSHOP: Effective use of nouns and noun phrases

How can I use nouns and noun phrases to summarise information?

Nouns are words that name people, places, events, ideas and objects. Nouns are important in titles and blurbs for nature documentaries because they sum up quickly what the story is about, where it takes place and who is involved, for example: Antarctica, penguins, journey, struggle.

Writers can expand the main ('head') noun into a **noun phrase**. They do this by adding words and phrases that give more specific information about the head noun, for example:

head noun ——→ beauty   *the sheer* beauty   *the sheer* beauty *of Antarctica*

Look at how this extra information can be placed before and after the head noun. Good writers choose nouns and noun phrases that are precise, pack in a lot of information and make us want to know more.

Look at the information that has been added to the head noun in these noun phrases. For each one, explain what the extra information tells you.

penguins living on the razor's edge

the **struggle** between life and death

a **journey** like no other on the planet

Look again at the blurb for *The Last Roar of the Lions*. The writer uses an expanded noun phrase about the lion: '*the most relentless* **fighter** *on the planet*'. Why do you think the writer chose the noun 'fighter'? What do the other details in the noun phrase tell you?

Using the head noun **survivor**, can you invent your own expanded noun phrase to describe the lion? Remember you can add details before and after the head noun.

CHECK YOUR WRITING

 In your blurb for *Polar Bear: Spy on the Ice*, highlight the nouns you have used. Are they as precise as you can make them? Have you expanded your nouns into noun phrases which add helpful and interesting information? Re-read your blurb and annotate it to show where your writing succeeds in making the film sound interesting and exciting. Make suggestions for alternative nouns or noun phrases to replace any which could be improved.

3 Describing nature by using comparisons

Learning objective

- Understand how writers and presenters use simile and metaphor to describe the natural world

Some things in nature are so incredible that they're difficult to imagine, let alone describe. Writers and presenters 'paint pictures' for us by using comparisons. For example, the astronomer Carl Sagan describes how tiny the Earth looks from space by comparing it to a dot or pixel – the smallest element that makes up a larger picture.

 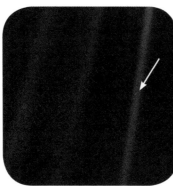

A ... the size of a marble, the most beautiful you can imagine. That beautiful, warm, living object looked so fragile, so delicate, that if you touched it with a finger it would crumble and fall apart.
(James Irwin)

B ... a sparkling blue and white jewel, a light, delicate sky-blue sphere laced with slowly swirling veils of white, rising gradually like a small pearl in a thick sea of black mystery.
(Edgar Mitchell)

Activity 1

1 Look at the photographs of Earth from space and read the astronauts' descriptions on the right.

   a Which description paints the best picture for you? Explain your choice.

   b Using either of the photographs to help you, invent two or three comparisons of your own to describe Earth as seen from space.

WRITER'S WORKSHOP: Using similes and metaphors to make comparisons

How can I use similes and metaphors to describe the natural world?

Good writers use **similes** and **metaphors** to draw attention to something special or unusual about a natural feature or creature. Look at this example:

> ... the explosion produced an immense wave in the sea. As it travelled towards the coast of Java, it became <u>a wall of water as high as a four-storey house</u>. It picked up a naval gunboat, carried it bodily nearly two kilometres inland and dumped it on top of a hill.
> (from *The Power of Krakatau* by David Attenborough)

Most people have never seen a tsunami so would find it difficult to picture one. Why does David Attenborough compare the tidal wave to a tall building? What picture does this give you?

For similes and metaphors to work, the objects being compared need to be connected in some way. The wave is the same *height* as a four-storey house, but it's also as *solid and dense* as a brick wall. What will happen when it crashes onto the shore? Can you make any connection with the destruction caused by a falling house?

Activity 2

1 Read these descriptions of sea creatures and for each one decide:

   a Which creature is being described? Match the correct letters and numbers.

   b What features of the creature are described and what are they compared to? Be as precise as possible.

   c Is it a good comparison? Explain your answer.

> A ... a long, torpedo-shaped body. At one end, surrounding a beak-like mouth strong enough to cut through steel cable, are five pairs of arms.

> B ... a few metres away was a pointed nose, and a mouth lined with razor-sharp teeth, coming at him.

> C ... the tail breaks the surface and rears up into the air, dripping with water. It is as wide as the wings of a small aircraft.

> 1 A great white shark

> 2 A blue whale

> 3 A giant squid

What do better writers do?

Better writers:

* use similes and metaphors to surprise or shock us: unusual comparisons can make us see the natural world in a new way.

Activity 3

1 Read the text below, adapted from *Things that go chomp in the night* by John Downer. The writer is describing creatures that live in our beds and come out every night to feed on our dead skin cells!

   a What are dustmites compared to? Can you find at least three different comparisons?

   b Explain which comparison you think is the most surprising or unusual.

2 Look at the photograph of a dustmite, magnified so that it's much larger than life.

   a Decide which feature of the dustmite to describe and what you can compare it to.

   b Write your own simile or metaphor describing this feature of the dustmite.

It isn't a pleasant thought, but you're never alone in bed. As you snuggle up among the sheets and blankets, an army of tiny refuse-collectors sifts and chews its way through your dreams.

Beneath the sheets of even the cleanest bed lurk thousands of eight-legged **scavengers**. We never notice our uninvited guests because each one is smaller than a speck of dust. They are only able to survive in this seemingly barren landscape because, each night, cells flake from our skin surface and shower down on them like **manna** from heaven. **Sustained** by this nutritious snowstorm, up to two million dustmites are able to survive in the average mattress ... they graze the vast **savannah** of our sheets, like herds of miniature **wildebeest**.

Glossary

scavengers: creatures that live off dead meat or rubbish

manna: in the Bible, the food provided for the Israelites in the wilderness

sustained: kept alive

savannah: plains in southern Africa

wildebeest: African animals, between an ox and an antelope

4 Getting up close

Learning objectives

- Understand how creatures and settings in the natural world are described in close detail

- Understand why writers choose the past or present tense

Film-makers and writers observe nature very carefully, giving us close-up views of the natural world. Photography can show us amazing and unusual things, like the inside of an ant colony or an eagle's-eye view of its prey. Vivid descriptions in books and voiceover scripts for documentaries let us share the writer's first-hand experiences and feelings about nature.

Activity 1

1 Read the interview with Verity White, a wildlife film-maker and producer. Using evidence from the interview, explain:

a What does Verity most and least enjoy about her job?

b Which of these skills and personal qualities are important in her job?

- patience
- courage
- knowledge about animals
- curiosity about nature.

c Would you like to do what she does? Explain why, or why not.

What do you get up to in an average day at work?
It differs all the time. Sometimes I'll spend the day walking through the Congo or getting stung by honeybees trying to get close-ups, other times I'm in the cosy edit in Bristol for weeks at a time.

What is the most challenging aspect of your job?
Being away from home for weeks at a time.

How long does it usually take to you to make a wildlife documentary?
It totally depends on time and budget. I made a film on African honeybees in a year; the 'Africa' series took four.

What is your favourite aspect of your job?
I love sitting in wild places, waiting for animals and behaviour. Sometimes it's for days at a time with hardly any sleep, but I get to make a connection with the earth that it's only possible to make by being totally still and silent. Your senses are heightened, smell, sight and hearing – everything becomes sharpened and for a brief time you can become a part of the landscape – it's magic! But it's not the only fun part: talking to scientists and finding amazing new stories is always exciting – marvelling at the animal kingdom then wondering how on earth to do the story justice on film is a fun challenge.

Have you ever had any dangerous experiences while filming wildlife?
Mostly whilst travelling – that's the most dangerous part! I climbed a tree once when an angry rhino got between me and the car. First and last tree I ever climbed...

Activity 2

1 In the 1960s, Jane Goodall observed chimp behaviour that had never been recorded before. She discovered that – like humans – chimpanzees can use tools. Read Jane's account of a chimp – David Graybeard – digging for insects. Imagine that you are producing a film about Jane Goodall and want to recreate this scene. You have 12 seconds of film you can use for it – enough for three or four frames only. Decide which details you will focus on, and sketch a storyboard for the scene.

I had had a frustrating morning, tramping up and down three valleys with never a sign or a sound of a chimpanzee ... not only weary but soaking wet from crawling through dense undergrowth. Suddenly I stopped, for I saw a slight movement in the long grass about sixty yards away. Quickly focusing my binoculars, I saw that it was a single chimpanzee, and just then he turned in my direction. I recognised David Graybeard. He was squatting beside the red earth mound of a termite nest. I saw him carefully push a long grass stem down into a hole in the mound. After a moment he withdrew it and picked something from the end with his mouth. I was too far away to make out what he was eating, but it was obvious that he was actually using a grass stem as a tool.

For an hour David feasted at the termite mound and then wandered slowly away. When I was sure he had gone, I went over to examine the mound ... I picked up one of his discarded tools and carefully pushed it into a hole myself. Immediately I felt the pull of several termites as they seized the grass, and when I pulled it out there were a number of worker termites and a few soldiers, with big red heads, clinging on...

WRITER'S WORKSHOP: Choosing which verb tense to use

Should I write in the past tense or the present tense?

Good writers know which **verb tense** to use in their writing and the effect they want to achieve. Jane Goodall is recounting an event from many years ago, so she chooses **past tense verbs** to tell the story:

> 'He <u>was squatting</u> beside the red earth mound of a termite nest. I <u>saw</u> him carefully push a long grass stem down into a hole in the mound.'

But in his account of dustmites, John Downer chooses **present tense verbs**:

> 'As you <u>snuggle</u> up among the sheets and blankets, an army of tiny refuse-collectors <u>sifts</u> and <u>chews</u> its way through your dreams.'

He wants us to feel that dustmites are in bed with us every night!

1 Read the second paragraph of Jane Goodall's account again, but change all the past tense verbs into the present tense as you read. What difference does it make?

2 Using present tense verbs, write a short script for the voiceover to accompany your storyboard. Write one sentence for each frame, for example: *The chimp <u>pokes</u> a grass stem into the termite mound and <u>holds</u> it there for a while.*

CHECK YOUR WRITING

➡ In your short voiceover script, highlight the verbs you have used. Are they in the present tense?
  • Read your script aloud, preferably to a partner so that you can ask for their feedback to these questions:
  • Are events clearly described?
  • Does the script sound like the voice of an expert on the natural world?

5 Writing your own close-up description of nature

Learning objective

- Understand how to write interesting descriptions of the natural world by choosing descriptive and precise noun phrases, verbs and comparisons

People who write about the natural world give us accurate facts about nature, but they make those facts come alive for us through interesting, detailed description.

Activity 1

1 Read this description of a velvet worm catching a beetle.

The velvet worm is one of the world's oldest **invertebrates**. It might be nearly blind, but it has a deadly weapon: slime. It shoots out **lasso-like ropes of glue** from a metre away, covering its victim in paralysing goo. This lethal adhesive dries in seconds, pinning the prey in a sticky net and giving the velvet worm time to reach it.

a List three facts about the velvet worm.

b Look carefully at the noun phrases highlighted in green. Which words tell you:

- that the velvet worm has existed for a very long time?
- that the velvet worm's victim is trapped and cannot move?
- that the velvet worm's victim will die?

2 The writer uses similes and metaphors to describe the velvet worm's slime:

- *lasso-like ropes of glue*
- *a deadly weapon*
- *a sticky net*
- *a lethal adhesive.*

Explain which you think is the best comparison.

3 The writer uses well-chosen verbs in the present tense to show how the velvet worm traps its prey. Look carefully at the verbs highlighted in pink. Which verb tells you:

- that the velvet worm traps its prey quickly?
- that the velvet worm uses a lot of slime to trap its prey?
- that the velvet worm's prey is trapped and cannot move?

Glossary

invertebrates: creatures that don't have a backbone

lasso: a loop of rope which is used to catch horses and cattle

Activity 2

Compare the two descriptions below of a cheetah running at speed.

1 What facts are used in both descriptions?

2 How does the voiceover script make the facts come alive for us? List examples of:

- noun phrases that describe parts of the cheetah's body
- verbs that show powerful movement.

3 The cheetah is compared to a fast car, a Porsche. How well does this comparison help you understand the cheetah's speed and strength?

4 Practise reading the voiceover script aloud. In order to make the cheetah sound fast and powerful, which words do you need to stress with your voice?

Entry in an online encyclopedia
The cheetah can run faster than any other land animal. It can accelerate from 0 to 100 km/h (62 mph) in 3 seconds. During a typical chase, its respiratory rate increases from 60 to 150 breaths per minute.

Voiceover script for documentary
From 0 to over 60 in under 3 seconds, she outperforms a Porsche. Extra-wide airways and outsized lungs allow her to take in more oxygen. Thrusting her forward are her huge leg muscles, powered by glycogen, nature's own rocket fuel.

Activity 3

1 Read this description of the naked mole rat.

   a List at least three facts about the creature.

   b How has the writer made the facts come alive? List examples of:

- noun phrases that describe its physical features
- verbs in the present tense that show how it moves
- similes or metaphors that show what it looks like or what it does.

Deep under the Saharan Desert, out of sight of predators, and away from the burning heat, the naked mole rat scurries through a maze of tunnels. This weird cold-blooded mammal, its skin hairless and wrinkled, looks like a sabre-toothed pale pink sausage! It can't see much with its tiny bead-like eyes, but navigates by feeling the walls of its underground world with bristly whiskers on its nose and tail.

Mole rats live in social groups called colonies, ruled over by a queen who is the only one to breed and give birth. Busy as workers on a building site, the rats spend up to 20 years repairing their underground caverns, shovelling earth with their ever-growing, sharp incisors.

Assessment: Describing nature

Learning objective

- Understand how to write a description of a creature or feature of the natural world in close-up detail

So far in this unit you have explored:

- the key features of presenting the natural world in film and writing
- selecting interesting facts and bringing them to life for the reader
- using noun phrases to pack a lot of information into a few words
- using comparisons – similes and metaphors – to describe nature
- using well-chosen verbs to show how something moves or acts
- using verbs in the past or present tense and keeping the choice consistent.

You will use all the skills you have developed so far to write a lively and detailed description of a creature or natural feature of your choice that will interest someone of your own age.

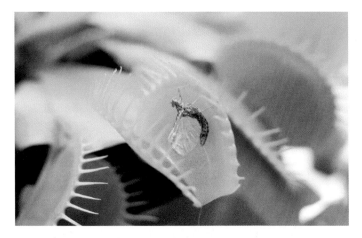

PLAN

Follow the steps below to collect your ideas and make important decisions before you start writing. You can use the ideas you have generated in previous lessons.

1 What kind of creature or feature will you describe? Something huge? tiny? scary? weird?

2 What is the most interesting thing about your creature or feature that you will describe in close-up detail? Choose one thing to research, for example: how your creature catches its prey, or where it lives; how powerful a tornado is, or how it moves.

3 Research this one aspect of your chosen creature or feature and choose two or three relevant and interesting facts to include in your description.

4 List the key vocabulary that you will use to bring the facts to life, especially noun phrases and verbs that pack in a lot of information.

5 Invent two or three similes or metaphors that will paint a clear picture of your creature or feature. Check that each comparison has a clear purpose, for example: to show *how small* something is, or *how quickly* it moves.

WRITE

Keep your plan in front of you to remind you of your choices. Read your writing out loud from time to time to check that it makes sense and to hear if it sounds lively and interesting.

Your task

Write a lively and detailed description of a creature or natural feature of your choice. Aim to write 100–120 words. Remember you are writing to interest someone of your own age. Write in the present tense.

REFLECT

Read your description aloud to hear whether it sounds lively and interesting. Choose a good example of each of the following from your writing:

- interesting facts
- noun phrases to add detailed information
- well-chosen verbs in the present tense
- comparisons to describe your creature or feature.

6 Sounding like an expert

Learning objectives

- Understand the conventions of a documentary voiceover script

- Understand how to use prepositional phrases to show where events take place

A voiceover script shows the words we hear as we are watching a nature documentary. The script is carefully matched to fit the frames of the film. It doesn't literally describe what we see, but instead tells an exciting story and highlights interesting facts about nature.

But he has a rival.

Once hunted to extinction in Yellowstone, the grey wolf is making a comeback, and he is hungry too.

In the wilderness of Yellowstone National Park, a grizzly is on the lookout for his next meal.

Activity 1

The grid shows still images from a documentary about grizzly bears and sentences from the voiceover script, but they are jumbled up.

1 Match each still image with the sentence that best fits it.

2 Decide the best sequence for the images and script.

3 Read the complete script aloud. How can you use your voice to make the documentary sound interesting and dramatic?

WRITER'S WORKSHOP: Documentary voiceover scripts

How can I sound like an expert on the natural world?

Voiceover scripts for documentaries have typical features:

- They use carefully chosen nouns and noun phrases to describe the creature and his behaviour clearly:

  A **grizzly** is on the **lookout** for his next **meal**.

- They mostly use verbs in the present tense to involve the viewer and describe the action as it happens:

  A grizzly **is** on the lookout for his next meal.

- They use **prepositional phrases** to make it clear where events are happening:

  In the wilderness of Yellowstone National Park, a grizzly is on the lookout for his next meal.

- There is often a problem or conflict in the story, which is signalled by using 'but':

  A grizzly is on the lookout for his next meal. **But** he has a rival.

Read aloud these two opening sentences for a documentary about gorillas. Choose the one that most sounds like the voice of an expert and explain your choice.

1 Gorillas live in forests somewhere in Africa but their food has almost run out because humans chopped down most of the trees.

2 Deep in the forests of the Congo live the world's last silverback mountain gorillas, but as more of the forest disappears to make way for humans, the gorillas face a fight for survival.

Activity 2

1 Read the voiceover script for *Year of the Tiger: End of the Road?*, a documentary about tigers in India, and find examples of:

   a present tense verbs to involve the viewer and to show that events are happening now

   b a prepositional phrase that shows where events are happening

   c 'but' used to signal a problem or conflict. Explain what the problem is.

2 Practise reading the script aloud to make the documentary sound interesting and dramatic. Use the punctuation to guide your voice.

3 Describe two still images that could match the script.

I'm right on the edge of Ranthambore National Park. This is where the tree line ends and the agricultural plains start. Thousands of people, thousands of livestock. The irony is that the tigers of Ranthambore have done so well inside that they are running out of space. But where are they going to go? There's just no more land and there are too many people. Are they sentenced to death? Can they ever survive?

WRITER'S WORKSHOP: Using prepositional phrases

How can I use prepositional phrases to make it clear where events take place?

Prepositions are small but useful words that can show where things happen, for example:

| at | in | on | under | below | beneath | between |

| inside | behind | across | among | around |

| beyond | underneath | along | within | near | from | to |

A prepositional phrase is formed from a preposition and a noun phrase or **pronoun** (e.g. 'it', 'him', 'them'):

| under the sea ice | in front of them | along the coast of California | across the valley |

| deep inside the forest clearing | from Pole to Pole | near its nest |

Good writers use prepositional phrases like signposts for readers, signalling a change of scene or direction.

Nature documentaries often start with a prepositional phrase, e.g. 'On the plains of the Serengeti, wildebeest are...' Why do you think they start like this?

Changing the position of the prepositional phrase can make a difference to the way the sentence sounds and to how clear the meaning is. Of the two sentences below, which version tells you most clearly where events take place? Which version do you think most sounds like the voice of an expert on the natural world?

1 A grizzly is on the lookout for his next meal in the wilderness of Yellowstone National Park.

2 In the wilderness of Yellowstone National Park, a grizzly is on the lookout for his next meal.

Activity 3

Read the fragments of the voiceover script below for the opening to a documentary on the wildlife of Africa.

1 Rewrite the script by adding prepositional phrases that:

a help the reader understand where the action is taking place

b make the documentary sound like the voice of an expert on the natural world.

Choose prepositional phrases from the list below or invent your own.

2 How many different versions of the script are possible? Experiment by changing the position of the prepositional phrases and decide which version sounds best.

> It is early morning. A lioness is playing with her cubs.
> A family of elephants gathers.

> at the edge of a waterhole

> on the vast plains of the Serengeti

> beneath a shady baobab tree

What do better writers do?

Better writers in voiceover scripts:

- use prepositional phrases to make it clear where events take place

- mostly use present-tense verbs to involve the viewer and describe the action as it happens

- use carefully chosen nouns and noun phrases to describe creatures clearly

- often signal a problem or issue by using 'but'.

7 Writing and performing a voiceover script

Learning objective

- Understand how to use punctuation to guide the reading voice

Punctuation helps us make sense of what we read by showing us where each sentence ends. But it does more than that. It also tells us *how* to read aloud – which words to stress for meaning and how to make our reading sound interesting and dramatic.

Activity 1

1 Read each of these sentences aloud, using the punctuation marks to guide how you say them.

   a These tigers are in trouble?

   b These tigers are in trouble!

   c Some animals – like these tigers – are in trouble.

   d Their world is shrinking: these tigers are in trouble.

   e Because their world is shrinking, these tigers are in trouble.

2 Choose any two of these sentences and explain:

   a which words you stress when you read each sentence

   b which sentence you think sounds the most interesting and dramatic, and why.

.	full stop
,	comma
?	question mark
!	exclamation mark
-	dash
:	colon

What do better writers do?

Better writers:

- know that punctuation changes the length, pace and rhythm of sentences and helps create the right tone and mood to match the subject, for example sadness, seriousness or humour

- use punctuation deliberately to control the length and shape of sentences for specific effects.

Activity 2

Read the sentences below, taken from a voiceover script for a humorous documentary about Benji, an ordinary dog with an extraordinary talent: playing rugby.

1   Count how many times the dog's name is used. Why do you think the writer uses his name so often?

2   Count the words in the longest sentence and in the shortest sentence. Why do you think the writer uses a lot of very short sentences?

3   Find an exclamation mark. There are several places where the writer could have used an exclamation mark, so why do you think it is used here?

4   Count how many *different* words are used in the final sentence. Why do you think the writer deliberately repeats words here? What is the effect of ending with a question mark?

5   Now use your answers to these questions to write a short paragraph that explains how the writer has used sentences and punctuation to make the script about Benji sound humorous.

> Take a look at Benji. Benji is no ordinary dog. Benji has a special talent. In fact, he's a champion. A rugby champion! Watch Benji race down the field and score a try. It's incredible. So – Benji can bark the bark, but can he walk the walk?

Activity 3

Here is another part of the voiceover script about Benji, taken from a humorous documentary.

1   Punctuate the script to make its meaning clear and to make it sound lively and humorous.

2   Practise reading your finished script aloud, using punctuation to highlight the meaning and to guide your voice. Does it sound lively and humorous?

> There is no stopping this boy he is as fast as lightning he leaves the others behind and yes he crosses the line what a try

CHECK YOUR WRITING

➡ In your voiceover script, highlight the punctuation you have used. Have you marked the end of each sentence so that the meaning is clear? Have you used a range of punctuation to show how to read the script?

8 Campaigning for nature

Learning objectives

- Understand how topics of concern in the natural world are presented in the media
- Understand how campaign logos and slogans sum up issues and attract the reader's attention

Activity 1

1 The issues below often make the headlines. Give each one a score from 1 to 3 to show how strongly you feel about it.

   1 = Not important
   2 = Quite important
   3 = Very important

2 Choose one of the issues and explain why it is, or is not, important to you.

Global warming, pollution, overpopulation – **issues** that affect the natural world are headline news.

World Population Hits 7 Billion

Ice Cap Meltdown

TROPIC OF CANCER

Oil Spill Devastates Gulf

A

> **MEMO**
>
> A hundred years ago there were 100,000 tigers in the wild. Today there are around 3,000. Tigers are killed for their body parts, used in traditional medicine.
> Stop this illegal trade. Save tigers now.

B

> **MEMO**
>
> Demand for palm oil – used in food and 'green' biofuel – has never been higher. But burning down rainforests to make way for oil palm plantations destroys natural habitats and adds to global warming. Protect the rainforests. Support life.

C

> **MEMO**
>
> Every year in the UK 18 million tonnes of food end up in landfill. While half the world is starving, the other half throws away more than it can eat. Love food. Hate waste.

Greenpeace; WWF (World Wide Fund for Nature); Friends of the Earth; RSPB (Royal Society for the Protection of Birds) – there are thousands of organisations campaigning to protect nature, and all of them want our help. So how do they attract readers' attention and get their message across?

giving nature a home

friends of the earth

see things differently

Activity 2

A **campaign** logo is the first thing most people notice. Logos mix images, names and slogans to get their message across very quickly.

1 Look at the logos opposite. For each one, time how quickly you can answer these questions:

a What is the name of the organisation?

b What does it campaign for?

c What message does the image give?

d If words are used, what is their message?

Glossary

issue: an important topic or problem which needs to be discussed

campaign: long-term action taken to achieve a goal

Activity 3

A campaign slogan is a catchy sentence that sums up an issue and tells you what you should do about it.

1 All of the slogans below give the message that we should recycle our rubbish.

a Vote for the one you think best conveys the message and explain your choice.

b Invent a campaign name and design a logo to go with the slogan you've chosen.

A Never refuse to recycle and reuse.

C Don't throw it away: use it another day.

D Recycle today for a cleaner tomorrow.

B Recycle your trash or you'll trash the Earth.

E Don't be a fool: recycling is cool!

Activity 4

Slogans use strong patterns of language that make them easy to remember.

1 Look again at the slogans about recycling. How many different patterns of language can you find? You could use a table like the one below to record more examples.

2 Invent a slogan that you think will encourage young people to recycle their rubbish. Write one sentence using 6–8 words.

3 Explain the patterns of language used in your slogan that make it easy to remember.

Pattern	Example
words that rhyme	
imperative verbs that tell you what to do	recycle
contrasts	today/tomorrow
two clauses joined with a colon	
abbreviations	

9 Getting involved

Learning objective

- Understand how campaign texts use personal pronouns, determiners which indicate possession, and imperative verbs to involve the reader and persuade them to take action

'Save the Arctic'; 'Wake up to Climate Change'; 'Clean up the World' – these are just some of the global campaigns that are trying to protect the future of the natural world. But how can just one person – you, for example – make a difference when the problems are so huge?

Activity 1

Read the newspaper article about a small town in Devon that hit the headlines for banning plastic bags.

1   Explain in two or three sentences the aim of Rebecca's campaign and why it's important to her.

2   Quote two pieces of evidence from the report to show that Rebecca's campaign has been successful.

3   Some people won't understand why plastic bags are harmful to wildlife. Using evidence from the article, invent a one-sentence slogan that will help people make the connection and persuade them to stop using plastic bags.

Town dumps plastic bags

Shopkeepers in the Devon town of Modbury are claiming a European first, by being entirely free of plastic bags. The idea has captured the imagination of communities across the UK who are now following suit.

Plastic bags have been consigned to the bin by traders in a Devon town in a bid to be more green. All 43 shopkeepers in Modbury are taking part, following a suggestion by a wildlife camerawoman who lives in the town.

Rebecca Hosking was moved to tears as she filmed marine life off Hawaii for the BBC2 programme, *Natural World*.

'What really brought it home for me was one day filming a turtle,' she said. 'It had a plastic bag in its mouth and was slowly dying. There was nothing we could do.

'I turned the camera off and just broke down crying. We see pretty grim things all the time, but this was man-made and it bugged me and I wanted to do something about it.'

When Rebecca, 33, returned home to Modbury, she set out on a mission to turn the town plastic-bag-free and managed to convince each and every trader to get on board. The town's Co-op has also joined in. On a busy day, the store could use 500 to 1,000 plastic bags, but those days are gone.

Now reusable cotton bags have been sent to every household. Plastic bag amnesty bins are dotted around Modbury, and those collected will be put to good use – in being recycled for furniture made entirely out of plastic waste.

'We never thought it would take off like this,' Rebecca told BBC Devon. 'I just wanted to do my bit for the environment, but it's just gone crazy. It's shown that local communities can really make a difference.'

WRITER'S WORKSHOP: Persuading the reader to act

How can I use pronouns, determiners and imperative verbs to involve my readers and persuade them to take action?

Because campaigns want your support, they speak directly to you and tell you what you can do to help.

- **Pronouns** and **determiners** like 'you', 'your', 'we', 'us', 'our', 'everybody', 'everyone' are used to make readers feel involved and responsible.

- **Imperative verbs** as in '<u>respect</u> your planet' and '<u>join</u> us' are used to tell readers what they should do.

Look at the campaign text below. All the personal pronouns and determiners are underlined.

Do <u>you</u> love <u>our</u> planet?

<u>Our</u> planet is a beautiful place. <u>Everybody</u> has the right to enjoy a clean and green environment. <u>We</u> must take care of <u>our</u> planet so that we can enjoy its beautiful scenery and superb wildlife now and in the future. Clean neighbourhoods are vital to <u>our</u> happiness. <u>We</u> want <u>everyone</u> to live in pleasant and attractive places. Imagine parks and beaches filled with litter. Would <u>you</u> want to spend time there? <u>We</u> can't let this happen. <u>We</u> need <u>your</u> help. Respect <u>your</u> planet.

Join <u>us</u> in showing how much <u>you</u> love <u>our</u> planet by donating to <u>our</u> charity today.

---

a The personal pronoun 'we' is used four times. Who does it refer to each time?

b The indefinite pronouns 'everybody' and 'everyone' are used. What does this tell you about the aims of the campaign?

c Count how many times 'you' and 'your' are used. Why do you think these pronouns and determiners are repeated so often?

d Look at the whole text and find the imperative verbs. What three things should the reader do?

e Write another short sentence to end the text, using an imperative verb to show the reader a fourth thing they can do to respect our planet. You could use any of these imperative verbs or choose your own:

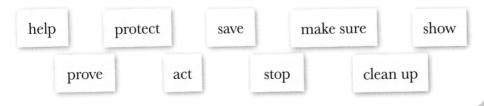

| help | protect | save | make sure | show |

| prove | act | stop | clean up |

What do better writers do?

Better writers:

- use pronouns and determiners to draw the reader in and involve them in the campaign issue

- use imperative verbs that make it clear what the reader should do.

Activity 2

Many students are involved in programmes in which they organise campaigns to improve their school environment, for example to save energy, stop food waste or create a garden.

1   Read the first draft of a campaign text from one student who wants to start an anti-litter campaign. What feedback would you give? You could explain what works well and what would make it even better.

2   The student's teacher said: 'You use facts well but the message about recycling isn't strong enough.' How far do you agree with this comment?

3   Rewrite the campaign text below to make it more persuasive, making sure you include:

  • pronouns and determiners that will involve the reader

  • imperative verbs that tell the reader what they should do.

There is too much litter in the school, especially at the end of break and lunchtime. Students drop cans, sweet wrappers, plastic cups and food containers. Litter blows around the playground and onto the school field. This makes the school look a mess. Even worse, plastic can harm or kill wildlife. The problem needs sorting out. Students should use the recycling bins.

CHECK YOUR WRITING

➔ In your improved draft of the campaign text, underline the pronouns, determiners and imperative verbs you have used. How well do you think your text will persuade students to stop dropping litter?

10 Patterns that persuade

Learning objective

• Understand how campaign texts use rhetorical devices to emphasise important information and persuade the reader to act

People have campaigned to protect the environment for a very long time, both to save wildlife and to fight for their own survival. In 1854, the Governor of Washington State in the USA wanted to buy a large area of land from the Native American tribes who lived there. Their leader, Chief Seattle, explained why 'the red man' did not want to sell their land to 'the white man'.

Activity 1

Read the extract from Chief Seattle's speech below and answer the questions.

1   Do you think Chief Seattle will sell the land? Provide evidence for your answer.

2   Chief Seattle tells the Governor of Washington, 'Our ways are different from your ways.' Explain at least three differences. You could use a table like the one below.

'The red man'	'The white man'
Thinks idea of owning land is strange.	Thinks land can be bought – or stolen – and owned.

3   The following sentence has been missed out from the speech:

> 'We are part of the earth and it is part of us.'

Decide the best point in the speech to place this sentence and explain your choice.

The Great White Chief in Washington sends word that he wishes to buy our land. We will consider your offer. For we know that if we do not sell, the white man may come with guns and take the land.

How can you buy or sell the sky, the warmth of the land? The idea is strange to us. If we do not own the freshness of the air and the sparkle of the water, how can you buy them? The earth does not belong to man; man belongs to the earth. This we know.

Our ways are different from your ways. Every part of the earth is sacred to my people. The perfumed flowers are our sisters; the deer, the horse and the great eagle are our brothers. The air is precious to the red man, for all things share the same breath.

The white man does not notice the air he breathes. The earth is not his brother but his enemy, and when he has conquered it, he moves on. He kidnaps the land from his children. His appetite will devour the earth and leave behind only a desert.

So if we sell you our land, love it as we've loved it. Care for it as we've cared for it. And with all your strength, with all your mind, with all your heart, preserve it for your children.

Activity 2

Chief Seattle uses rhetorical devices that emphasise his points and help us remember them.
Look at the table below, which shows the devices used in Chief Seattle's speech.

1 a For each rhetorical device, find and list at least one more example from the speech.

  b Choose one rhetorical device and invent an example that could be added to the speech.

  c Suggest where in the speech you would place your new sentence and explain why.

Rhetorical devices	Example
A rhetorical question that makes the reader think	How can you buy or sell the sky, the warmth of the land?
Imperative verbs that tell the reader how they should act	So if we sell you our land, <u>love</u> it as we've loved it.
Simple sentences with only one verb to sum up and emphasise ideas	Every part of the earth <u>is</u> sacred to my people.
Parallelism of key ideas and sentence structures	The earth does not belong to man; man belongs to the earth.
Triads or 'rule of three': three words, phrases or clauses listed for emphasis	...love it...Care for it...preserve it...

What kind of footprint leaves a mark on the earth even though it can't be seen? It's called a carbon footprint. When we burn fossil fuels – like coal, oil and gas – carbon dioxide gets into the atmosphere, and it's making our planet dangerously warm. Our carbon footprint measures how much CO_2 we create as energy waste, and a big carbon footprint is bad for the Earth.

Waste a little less energy every day: walk instead of going in the car; switch off the lights when you leave a room; put on a jumper when you're cold instead of turning up the heat.

We all leave footprints on the earth. Just make sure yours are small ones.

Activity 3

1 Read the text above which comes from a website promoting 'green' energy use.

  a How many of the rhetorical devices in the table above can you find in this text?

  b How well do you think this text:
   - tells the reader what a carbon footprint is?
   - persuades the reader to help the planet by saving energy?

Activity 4

Write the text of a short speech that will persuade students in your school to save energy and reduce the school's carbon footprint. Use carefully chosen sentence patterns and rhetorical devices to emphasise your points and persuade your reader to take action.

CHECK YOUR WRITING

With a partner, read your speech aloud and ask for feedback that answers these questions:
- Are my points clear?
- Have I persuaded you to save energy at school?
- Which is the most persuasive sentence and why?

11 Making links

Learning objective

- Understand how campaign texts connect ideas together effectively

'Your planet needs you'; 'You can make a world of difference'; 'Keep *your* world green and clean' – campaign slogans and texts often make strong links between an individual's actions and their global effects. One way of doing this is to link facts and actions.

PAIR A

PAIR B

PAIR C

Activity 1

1 Look carefully at the linked pairs of photographs on these pages.

For each pair of photographs:

a Describe what is shown.

b Explain the issue you think might link them together.

c Choose one pair and write a caption that sums up the issue.

Activity 2

1 Match the facts and actions in the table below.

a Explain the clues you used to do this.

b Read the matching facts and actions aloud and list the key words that are repeated.

> **What do better writers do?**
>
> Better writers:
>
> • select powerful and interesting facts that make the reader think about the issue
>
> • link ideas clearly so the reader can follow them.

Facts	Actions
Burning fossil fuels like coal, oil and natural gas releases CO_2 into the atmosphere, making the Earth warmer and contributing to climate change.	We could avoid throwing away plastic by re-using plastic bags, recycling plastic bottles and campaigning for supermarkets to use less packaging.
10 million tonnes of plastic litter ends up in the world's oceans every year, poisoning fish and other marine animals.	We need to stop the population of the world growing so fast and stop richer countries using more than their share of the Earth's resources.
The population of the world is currently using up the natural resources of the Earth 1.5 times faster than they can be regrown.	We could depend less on energy from fossil fuels by insulating our homes and using solar panels.

An important way of linking ideas in sentences and paragraphs is by using **synonyms** – different words that are similar in meaning. For example, if you were writing about the problems caused by litter, you could also use the nouns 'trash', 'rubbish', 'packaging', 'waste'. If you were writing about how to recycle litter, you could also use the verbs 're-use', 'save', 'recover', 'reclaim'.

Activity 3

1   Look at the jumbled lists of words below. Each of the four topic words in **bold** has three synonyms or related words. Match them together in lists.

rising   **people**   globe   increasing   stores   **world**   expanding   communities

stocks   population   **resources**   earth   supplies   planet   societies   **growing**

2   Look at your lists. What campaign topic links them all? Choose the best topic sentence from the list below.

   a   Many animal species are dying out.

   b   Population growth is using up the Earth's resources.

   c   Pollution in cities is a growing problem.

WRITER'S WORKSHOP: Linking ideas effectively

How can I use conjunctions and conjuncts to link ideas?

Conjunctions and **conjuncts** are words that are used to link ideas. Conjuncts can be used at the start of a new paragraph or sentence to link ideas across the whole text, for example:

| Firstly | Secondly | Next | Moreover | However | Finally |

Conjunctions link ideas within the same sentence.

How can I use coordinating conjunctions to link ideas in the same sentence?

Coordinating conjunctions 'and', 'but' and 'or' are used to join ideas of equal importance and balance.

'and' joins similar ideas:

> The human population is rising **and** animal habitat is disappearing.

'but' joins contrasting ideas:

> A hundred years ago there were 100,000 tigers in the wild **but** today there are only around 3,000.

'or' shows a choice:

> We can insulate our homes **or** install solar panels.

How can I use subordinating conjunctions to link ideas in the same sentence?

| if | because | when | while | as | although | since |

Subordinating conjunctions are used to join ideas where one idea is dependent on the other or one thing causes another:

> Animals lose their habitat **when** the human population expands.

> **Because** the sea ice is melting, life in the Arctic is changing.

> We can all save water **if** we fix leaking taps.

Subordinating conjunctions can go at the start of a sentence or in the middle of a sentence.

Activity 4

1 Look at the three sentences below.

  a Join them into one sentence using coordinating and subordinating conjunctions.
    Try at least three different versions.

  b Choose the one version you think best connects the ideas in the sentence and explain
    your choice.

The world is using up too much energy.

We are not in a hopeless situation.

We can all make helpful changes to our lifestyle.

2 Look again at the table on page 71, where you matched facts and actions. Join the
  statements together by using coordinating and subordinating conjunctions. How many
  different versions can you make?

12 Writing to save the world

Learning objective

- Understand how to plan a persuasive campaign text

Campaigns to protect the natural world are supported by people across the globe, from famous celebrities to students at school. What links them all is powerful writing. Web pages, tweets, blogs, newsletters, leaflets, press releases, campaign letters and emails – all of these use powerful writing to inform you about an issue and persuade you to help.

The Prince's Rainforest Project

Leonardo DiCaprio supports the NRDC project

Lily Allen supports the WWF and Sky's Rainforest Rescue Project

Joanna Lumley supports the animal welfare project, Stop Live Exports

Activity 1

Many organisations campaign for nature by holding a special annual event. Every year the United Nations holds a World Environment Day to tell people about global issues and show how they can make a difference. A different theme is chosen each year.

Look at the logo below for the 2013 World Environment Day.

1   What do you think the campaign is about? Choose from the list below and explain your choice.

   a   Eating healthily

   b   Spending less money on food

   c   Not wasting food

2   Read the facts used in the Think.Eat.Save campaign, below.

   a   Which fact most surprised you?

   b   Which fact do you think would best persuade people to join the campaign?

THINK·EAT·SAVE
REDUCE YOUR FOODPRINT

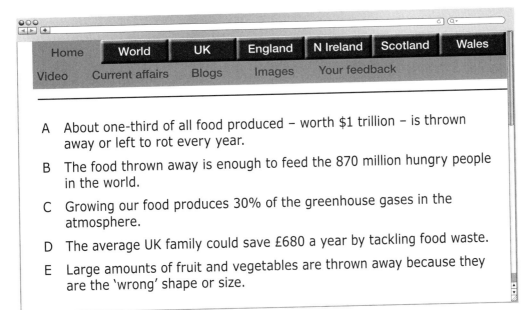

| Home | World | UK | England | N Ireland | Scotland | Wales |

Video   Current affairs   Blogs   Images   Your feedback

A   About one-third of all food produced – worth $1 trillion – is thrown away or left to rot every year.

B   The food thrown away is enough to feed the 870 million hungry people in the world.

C   Growing our food produces 30% of the greenhouse gases in the atmosphere.

D   The average UK family could save £680 a year by tackling food waste.

E   Large amounts of fruit and vegetables are thrown away because they are the 'wrong' shape or size.

Activity 2

1 Read the campaign text below about WWF's annual Earth Hour event.

2 Explain in one or two sentences what Earth Hour is.

3 The writer of the campaign text has chosen language carefully to persuade readers to join the campaign. The text has been annotated to show some of these choices. Look at the annotations and answer the questions.

   a Synonyms and related words that describe something extraordinary. Can you find two similar words?

   b Pronouns and determiners used to involve the reader. Who does 'we' refer to? Why is it used so often?

   c Triad/rule of three. What idea is stressed through repetition?

   d A rhetorical question that makes the reader think about the answer. Why do you think this is also a very short sentence?

   e Find the two imperative verbs used in the last sentence. Why do you think they are used at the end of the text?

WWF's Earth Hour is a unique annual phenomenon that focuses the world's attention on our amazing planet and the need to protect it. At 8.30 pm on 23 March hundreds of millions of people turned off their lights for one hour, on the same night, all across the world. For Earth Hour 2013, the focus is on the kind of energy we use. To create a better future for our planet we need to move away from dirty fossil fuels and on to clean green renewable energy which works with the awesome power of nature, not against it. Why take part? Because our brilliant planet needs you. In the UK we're consuming three times our fair share of the planet's natural resources. We want the government to commit to making our electricity system virtually carbon-free by 2030. Together we have the power to make change happen. Sign up to WWF's Earth Hour now and show your support for the switch to a better energy future.

In this unit, you've seen how campaigns use powerful writing to protect the future of the planet. Now it's your turn to write to save the world!

Assessment: Writing a campaign text

Learning objective

- Understand how to write a campaign text that informs your readers and persuades them to act

In the last few lessons of this unit you have explored:

- typical issues in campaigns to protect the natural world
- how campaign logos and slogans attract the reader's attention
- using pronouns, determiners and imperative verbs to involve the reader and persuade them to take action
- using rhetorical devices for emphasis and persuasion
- linking ideas together.

You will use all the skills you have developed so far to write a campaign text to save the natural world. You may not be able to launch a global campaign, but you could start a successful campaign for nature in your school.

PLAN

Follow the steps below to collect ideas and make important decisions before you start writing.

1   What issue will you choose for your campaign? Saving tigers? Protecting the rainforests? Creating a 'green' school? You can use any of the ideas in this unit or choose an issue in the natural world that concerns you.

2   Research facts about your issue and choose the ones that will best inform students about it and persuade them to support your campaign.

3   Decide what kind of event you want to hold at school to promote your campaign.

4   Decide on a short, catchy slogan that will sum up the campaign issue and help to promote the event.

5   Plan how many paragraphs you will need in your letter. You will need to:

- explain the name and aim of your campaign
- explain what the issue is and why you think it's important
- explain what event you want to hold at school and why you want to hold it.

WRITE

You are now ready to write your campaign letter.

Your task:

Write a letter to the headteacher of your school, explaining your campaign to save the natural world and persuading the school to support it. Use 200-250 words.

In your letter you should:

• explain clearly what the issue is

• persuade the headteacher to support your campaign.

You should include a campaign name and slogan.

You can include a logo design if you like.

You can send your letter by post or by email.

The RSPCA has some useful tips for campaign letter-writing:

• Always include your name and address.

• Get to the point quickly and deal with one clear topic: 'I am concerned about...'

• Explain how you are affected by the issue: 'I am shocked that... I am saddened by... I strongly believe that...'

• Explain what your views are: 'We should all be concerned about the issue of recycling because...'; 'Unless we protect endangered species like tigers...'

• Be polite and formal, not rude or aggressive: remember, you are asking the headteacher to support your campaign and promote it at school.

• Be positive at the end of your letter or email: 'I look forward to hearing from you'; 'I will be able to answer any questions you have.'

• Use language persuasively — remember you are competing with other students and want the headteacher to choose *your* campaign to promote.

REFLECT

Read your letter aloud to hear whether it sounds informative and persuasive. Have you:

• used paragraphs to make the letter clear and easy to follow

• used pronouns, determiners and imperative verbs to involve the reader and persuade them to take action

• used rhetorical devices for emphasis and persuasion: repetition of key ideas and parallel sentence structures; rhetorical questions to make the reader think; triads or rule of three; simple sentences with one verb to sum up and emphasise ideas

• linked ideas together, including use of conjunctions?

Give a good example of each of these from your writing.